FireNotes

Fireground Skills ~ Fireground Language

MW00641551

Firefighter Rescue & Rapid Intervention Teams

Saving One of Our Own

Written by
Jim McCormack

P.O. Box 1852 • Indianapolis, IN 46206
http://www.fdtraining.com

Lenny Steed

Third Printing—Revised Edition, 2009

Cover Photo © Steve Spak

Published by
Fire Department Training Network, Inc.
P.O. Box 1852
Indianapolis, IN 46206

ISBN 0-9719788-2-4

ABOUT THE AUTHOR

Jim McCormack has been a firefighter for 15 years and is currently a lieutenant with the Indianapolis Fire Department. Jim is the founder and president of the Fire Department Training Network, a membership network dedicated to firefighter training, and author of the FireNote, *Firefighter Survival.*

ABOUT THE
FIRE DEPARTMENT TRAINING NETWORK

The Fire Department Training Network, Inc. is a not-for-profit training organization dedicated to training firefighters. The Network produces results-oriented, reality-based, training material for firefighters and fire departments, including a monthly newsletter and fire department training package, *FIRESCUE Interactive* and the *FIRESCUE Interactive Department Trainer.*

The Network conducts courses and seminars across the country as well as ongoing training courses at FIRESCUE USA, its national firefighter training academy, located just outside of Indianapolis, Indiana.

For more information on the Network visit:
www.fdtraining.com

Fire Notes

Fireground Skills ~ Fireground Language

IN THIS FIRENOTE:

■ **FIREFIGHTER RESCUE: THE ULTIMATE FIREGROUND CHALLENGE**

■ **FIREFIGHTER RESCUE**
SEARCHING FOR A FIREFIGHTER;
ASSESSING, STABILIZING AND PACKAGING A FIREFIGHTER;
FIREFIGHTER RESCUE AND REMOVAL TECHNIQUES

■ **RAPID INTERVENTION TEAMS**
WHY?; THE RAPID INTERVENTION TEAM; RIT TOOLS AND STAGING;
PREPARING THE FIREGROUND; RESPONDING TO A FIREGROUND MAYDAY;
COMMANDING RAPID INTERVENTION OPERATIONS

■ **FIREFIGHTER RESCUE AND RIT TRAINING SESSIONS**

WWW.FDTRAINING.COM

DEDICATION

This FireNote is dedicated to you, the reader, for continuing to pursue a safer fireground through training.

Pass on your knowledge, it just might make a difference in the life of a firefighter!

Table of Contents

FORWARD 1

FIREFIGHTER RESCUE:
THE ULTIMATE FIREGROUND CHALLENGE 3

PART I: FIREFIGHTER RESCUE 13

SEARCHING FOR A FIREFIGHTER 17

ASSESSING, STABILIZING & PACKAGING 29

FIREFIGHTER RESCUE AND REMOVAL TECHNIQUES 55

PART II: RAPID INTERVENTION TEAMS 107

WHY DO WE NEED RAPID INTERVENTION TEAMS? 111

THE RAPID INTERVENTION TEAM 117

RAPID INTERVENTION TEAM TOOLS AND STAGING 135

PREPARING THE FIREGROUND — PROACTIVE RIT TASKS 145

RESPONDING TO A MAYDAY — THE RIT DEPLOYMENT 159

COMMANDING RAPID INTERVENTION OPERATIONS 167

PART III: TRAINING SESSIONS 175

FIREFIGHTER RESCUE &
RAPID INTERVENTION TEAM TRAINING SESSIONS 177

FORWARD

This FireNote deals with one of the most stressful situations you'll ever encounter during your career as a firefighter — rescuing one of your own! While it may be possible to complete an entire career without performing a firefighter rescue, the reality is that you may have to perform one the next time you respond.

Failure to plan for a potential firefighter rescue is planning to fail. There are no second chances on the fireground!

Specifically, this FireNote deals with two separate, yet dependent, topics:

- Firefighter Rescue

- Rapid Intervention Teams

While the two topics go hand-in-hand, a thorough knowledge and understanding of the individual skills involved in rescuing a firefighter is a pre-requisite for any successful rapid intervention team operation.

The most important issue regarding firefighter rescue and rapid intervention team operations is that prevention is the key! If you can prevent an emergency situation from developing then you limit the chances of having to perform a rescue. If, however, you can't prevent the situation—or the events were out of your control to begin with—previous hands-on training with different firefighter rescue skills and rapid intervention team scenarios just may save the life of a firefighter.

Reading a book, by itself, can not make you proficient at performing firefighter rescues. The rescue techniques described and shown in this FireNote must be practiced in the training environment under the supervision of a qualified fire department trainer who is familiar with them. This FireNote reviews firefighter rescue and rapid intervention team operations but it can not and does not replace the required training that must be performed in order to become proficient at these operations.

1

FIREFIGHTER RESCUE:
The Ultimate Fireground Challenge

WHAT IS IT?

Firefighter rescue is one of the most challenging situations you'll ever face on the fireground. The only event likely to be more challenging and stressful than performing a firefighter rescue is an individual fireground emergency. When faced with an individual emergency your ability to calmly deal with the situation will be your most difficult obstacle. When faced with rescuing a firefighter—teamwork, communication and focus will be the most difficult factors to control.

Firefighter rescue involves assisting and/or removing a firefighter from a troubled location or situation on the fireground. The rescue may be as simple as guiding the firefighter to the outside (safety) or as complicated as extricating the firefighter from a collapse or entanglement, securing his air supply with a new source, and removing him from the structure. Sometimes the complexity is based on the situation and sometimes it's based on a lack of preparation.

FIREFIGHTER RESCUE CAN BE BROKEN DOWN INTO THREE POSSIBLE SCENARIOS:

1. Assisting/rescuing a member of your own crew;

2. Assisting/rescuing a firefighter encountered during interior operations; or

3. Assisting/rescuing a firefighter when performing as part of a rapid intervention team.

Whenever any of the above rescue situations are encountered on the fireground, the firefighter(s) performing the rescue must remain calm, communicate the situation, and use teamwork and previous training to resolve the problem.

Before discussing each of the three rescue scenarios, let's talk a little about the name of the rescue team. In a nutshell, the name of the team doesn't make any bit of difference! Rapid Intervention Team (RIT), Rapid Intervention Crew (RIC), Firefighter Assist and Search Team (FAST), or whatever else you call it in your area simply refers to the team of firefighters who are standing by ready to rescue a firefighter in trouble. *The most important*

issue regarding the team is their competency—not their name. For consistency sake it would be nice to use the same term across the country but that issue is left for others. Let's focus on the proficiency of the team!

ASSISTING A MEMBER OF YOUR OWN CREW

While operating on the fireground a member of your crew may run into trouble and require assistance. A simple entanglement, a low air supply, a partial collapse...or any number of other things may occur which cause the member to require assistance. Assisting the firefighter may be simple and allow your company to continue operations—or it may require you to issue a fireground MAYDAY while you attempt to

resolve the problem. No matter what the situation, immediate assistance and rescue of the firefighter comes from the crew members operating with the member.

ASSISTING A FIREFIGHTER ENCOUNTERED DURING INTERIOR OPERATIONS

While performing on the fireground you may encounter another firefighter who is in trouble. Solving the firefighters' problem should become your number one priority but you must also communicate the problem to Command so that help (RIT) can be deployed. While assisting a firefighter encountered during interior operations will take precedence over all other operations, the original fireground functions (attack, search, etc.) must be continued or you're likely to become part of a larger problem. Tunnel vision during this type of rescue may jeopardize all firefighters on the fireground.

ASSISTING A FIREFIGHTER AS PART OF A RAPID INTERVENTION TEAM

Performing a firefighter rescue as part of a rapid intervention team is a fireground operation that will require precise communication, solid fireground skills, teamwork and, more than likely, additional rescue teams. The rapid intervention team operates under the most intense fireground conditions—a firefighter in trouble—and must locate, stabilize/package, and remove the firefighter (or crew). These stressful conditions (as with all firefighter rescue situations) require solid leadership and previous training if there is to be any chance of success.

A known emergency—a firefighter in trouble—active fireground conditions and a time-sensitive rescue mission all combine to make a rapid intervention team operation one of the most difficult missions encountered on the fireground. Training, preparation, and a proactive attitude (by both firefighters and the department) are essential components of any successful firefighter rescue.

WHEN WILL IT HAPPEN?

1992 — Indianapolis

1995 — Pittsburgh

1998 — New York

1999 — Worcester

2000 — Alabama

2001 — Phoenix

2002 — St. Louis

There are many more cities and departments that could be listed.

It's happened before and it will happen again. Has it happened in your department? Could it? YES!

A fireground emergency could happen, resulting in the need for a firefighter rescue, the next time you respond. Many firefighters feel that it will never happen to them, for whatever reason, but they couldn't be further from the truth. There are a number of variables that lead to an emergency, some can be controlled and some can't, and the individual firefighter is only one of them. Don't fall victim to complacency when it comes to planning for firefighter rescue.

Every year an average of 100 firefighters die in the line of duty. 30 – 40 of those firefighters are performing fireground operations when it happens. That's one firefighter every 10 days, give or take. When was your last work shift? When was your last fire?

FIREFIGHTER FATALITIES

1991	108
1992	77
1993	81
1994	105
1995	102
1996	98
1997	99
1998	93
1999	112
2000	103
2001	441
2002	102

SOURCE: USFA

A firefighter may need assistance the next time you respond. Are you and your department ready? Advancing a hose line, searching for victims, performing ventilation, searching for the seat of the fire—trouble can occur at any time on the fireground. There's just no way to accurately predict when it will happen. Anticipate trouble on every response and prepare for firefighter rescue before it's needed.

WHAT WILL A FIREFIGHTER RESCUE REQUIRE?

A Firefighter rescue requires information, skilled fire-fighters and a lot of luck. That's right, luck! No matter how much information there is about the situation, no matter how skilled the firefighters performing the rescue are, things still have to go your way for success. Whatever you call it—luck, good fortune, catching a few breaks—if things don't fall into place then it still may not work out. However, prior training in firefighter rescue skills and techniques is an essential component of a successful rescue.

Information

A successful firefighter rescue requires a constant flow of information. Where is the firefighter? What happened to cause the emergency? Can the firefighter help with the rescue? Can the firefighter help you in pinpointing his exact location? All of these questions, and more, must be answered as soon as possible during the emergency. A continuous flow of information, and updates, must continue throughout the emergency.

Skilled Firefighters

Let's face it, when it's time to rescue one of your own you better know what you're doing! This will be the most stressful situation you've ever been a part of and it's not the time to figure out you're not ready for it.

A solid knowledge of basic firefighting skills—engine work, truck work, rescue work, building construction, fire behavior, size-up, communications, etc.—is essential if you're going to pull off a rescue. There's no time to 'learn as you go' when a firefighters' life is on the line. Sure, you may come up with some new techniques (based on what you know) when performing the rescue but they usually come from a modification of something you already know.

Unfortunately, many departments just randomly assign companies as rapid intervention teams to comply with national standards and department standard operating procedures. That's liability not rescue! Being a part of a firefighter rescue team requires a personal commitment that you'll be up to the task and provide the best possible chance for a successful outcome. It's a bond between the rescuer(s) and the firefighter(s) being rescued.

SUCCESS VERSUS FAILURE

There's no doubt that luck plays a role in any successful firefighter rescue but the commitment of the individual firefighters and the entire department plays a more important role.

Supporting a firefighter rescue and rapid intervention team program requires more than simply writing it down and providing a 'lip service' response. It requires a conscious effort on the part of all involved—along with frequent and realistic training—to be prepared for whatever might happen.

Being prepared means having a basic procedure in place, having a rapid intervention team on the fireground standing by and ready to perform, having all firefighters trained in individual survival and firefighter rescue skills, and, most of all, trying to prevent fireground emergencies by being proactive both before and during the fire.

THERE ARE NO SECOND CHANCES!

There are no second chances when it comes to rescuing a firefighter. A fireground emergency may happen at any time and a team must be standing by and capable of solving the emergency.

Being part of a rapid intervention team is not the most glorious assignment—a successful operation means you won't get 'a piece of the action'—but it's the most important assignment on the fireground when something goes wrong. There are absolutely no excuses, NONE, for not being 100% ready to rescue one of our own on the fireground!

Sometimes no matter how much preparation has been done, things still go wrong, but we all know the difference between a true tragedy and a failure to prepare. *There are no second chances.*

FIREFIGHTER RESCUE & RAPID INTERVENTION TEAMS

12

PART I
FIREFIGHTER
RESCUE

Firefighter Rescue Skills

Firefighter rescue skills include those skills and techniques required to locate and remove a firefighter. Part I of this FireNote deals with the following rescue skills:

■ Searching for a firefighter

■ Assessing, stabilizing and packaging a firefighter

■ Firefighter rescue and removal techniques

Proficiency at these skills is a must if firefighters are to be successful operating as part of a rapid intervention team.

2

SEARCHING
FOR A FIREFIGHTER

One of the most difficult task assignments during a fireground emergency is searching for a lost or missing firefighter! Organized chaos is the term that may best describe this operation. Adrenaline will be flowing, to say the least, and emotions will be difficult to control. Discipline is a must. Training is the key to making this a successful operation. When searching for a missing firefighter everyone seems to forget the basics! Here's a few points to consider when faced with this difficult assignment.

USE A SYSTEMATIC SEARCH

Don't let emotions control the event. Sure, you'll probably use a combination of search techniques to find the firefighter — but the foundation of the search will be based on basic search and rescue skills. ***Remember the basics!***

SPEED IS CRITICAL - *IT'S A FIREFIGHTER*

This goes without saying — but it's often overlooked. Conducting a primary search for a civilian is not the same as conducting a search for a missing firefighter. For starters, you know when the firefighter got there and, hopefully, what probable location he may be in. Don't forget, it must still be a thorough, systematic, search—*but speed is critical!*

PERFORM A SEARCH SIZE UP

Get as much information as possible before, and during, the search. If you're a member of the RIT then this RECON is part of your fireground assignment. Consider some of the following pieces of information.

■ Who are you looking for?

■ What was the assignment?

■ What's happening on the fireground?

Who are you looking for?

This is an important piece of information for a few reasons. One obvious reason is that the person may not be missing (it's happened)! Another reason is that it may help identify the location, or possible location, of the firefighter. How aggressive is the person? How competent is the person? How fast does the person move inside structures under these conditions? It may be possible to answer some of these questions and help determine a probable location.

What was the assignment?

What was the missing firefighter doing? Attack? Ventilation? Search? By knowing the assignment and combining that with the type of building, the location and extent of the fire, the probable location of occupants, and overall fireground conditions (visibility issues, known hazards, etc.) it may be possible to narrow down the search area.

What's happening on the fireground?

Are conditions improving? Are they getting worse? Has any progress been made since the first units arrived? *What are the fire conditions? What are the structural conditions? What is the condition of the firefighters?* All these questions, and more, will give an indication of the conditions that may have lead to the problem. This information will also assist in developing the search plan.

> **In a true missing firefighter emergency use any and all means to locate the missing firefighter.**

Consider using the **LUNAR** acronym to remember the basic information to be gathered for a missing firefighter.

L   LAST KNOWN LOCATION

U   UNIT NUMBER

N   NAME

A   ASSIGNMENT

R   RADIO EQUIPPED

HAVE A PLAN

Searching for a firefighter, as stated above, will be one of the most difficult assignments of your career. How will the search be conducted? How many are in the search team? Who's the leader? What is each member responsible for? Who's responsible for knowing the way out? Who will maintain contact with Command? Does the search end when the firefighter is found or will someone search for the closest exit? What is the procedure if the search party gets split up? Who's responsible for keeping the search team intact (everybody)? The list goes on.

Plan the search. Know what will be done when the firefighter is found. Communication is critical.

USE A TAG LINE

A tag line should be used during all firefighter rescue and rapid intervention team operations. The tag line is

SELECTING AND USING A TAG LINE

A tag line should be used any time the rapid intervention team is deployed to search for a firefighter. The tag line should be tied-off at the point of entrance. This line serves two distinct purposes. First, it provides the search team with a direct route to safety. Second, it provides a direct route for additional help that may be called in to assist with the rescue.

The tag line should be long enough (a 200 foot rope works well), not too big or bulky, and stored in a bag that can be carried or clipped to the firefighter. For convenience, many  departments use 1/2-inch rescue or utility rope as a tag line but the problem with this rope is that it's too bulky. A smaller rope is much more manageable and serves the same purpose.

The first and most important step when using a tag line is to tie it off at the point of entry. The line should be secured to the outside of the structure by the person responsible for deploying it. The RIT Officer or Navigation position

of the RIT *(see The Rapid Intervention Team)* will be assigned this task.

The rope must also be managed—which is a difficult task. Managing the tag line involves both letting out and taking up rope. The idea is that the rope provides a direct line to the search team or firefighter. If the line goes in and back out of a room then it must be collected. **Rope management, or lack of it, is probably the biggest reason that teams fail to use a tag line.** Training increases rope management skills!

a tether to the outside (or a safe area). The tag line is not the same as a personal search line or individual search lines used during a team search operation (see below).

SEARCH TECHNIQUES...

Searching for a missing firefighter will draw from all previous fireground skills and training, guaranteed! Some of the following techniques, coupled with basic search and rescue skills, may assist in locating the missing firefighter.

- Conventional Right-/Left-Handed Search
- PASS Device-Assisted Search
- Radio-Assisted Feedback Search
- Rope-Assisted Search
- Thermal Camera-Assisted Search

Conventional Right-/Left-Hand Search

This is basic search and rescue and will be the foundation of the firefighter search. Some of the other techniques listed below will allow you to minimize the use of the conventional right-/left-hand pattern but there will be times during the search that it will be used.

PASS Device Assisted Search

When searching for an activated PASS device the search team may be able to move quicker throughout the structure. The basic concept of this search is that the team listens for, and moves toward, the activated PASS. This is easier said than done when all the other fireground noises are included. This is not a search by committee! Listening for, and moving toward, the PASS is a difficult task — to say the least. One member of the

search team must be responsible for determining the direction of travel. Stop, Listen, Move. If the sound is getting louder then continue in that direction. If the sound is diminishing then regroup, move back to where the sound was louder and move toward the sound. *Practice this technique!*

Radio-Assisted Feedback Search

If the missing firefighter is equipped with a radio, and the radio is turned on (volume up), it may be possible to create an improvised alerting device. How? By keying two portable radios close together a squelching sound is created on other radios. The search team may be able to stop, turn all radios down, key two radios together and listen for the squelching sound created. Difficult? Yes! Will it work? Maybe! Is it worth a shot? You bet!

Rope-Assisted Search

When talking about rope-assisted searches there are usually two types discussed; personal search ropes and

team, or large-area, search.

Personal search ropes may assist the search team by allowing members to quickly branch off to search areas where members can't keep in contact. By incorporating a search rope — that tethers members back to the main search party — the entire search team doesn't have to move in that direction.

Team search involves a complete rope-based search system. The concept involves a main guide line, controlled by the lead person, and individual (personal) search lines of a known length that become appendages to  the guide line. A half-moon search pattern, off of the guide line, is used by the searching firefighters to cover the area being searched.

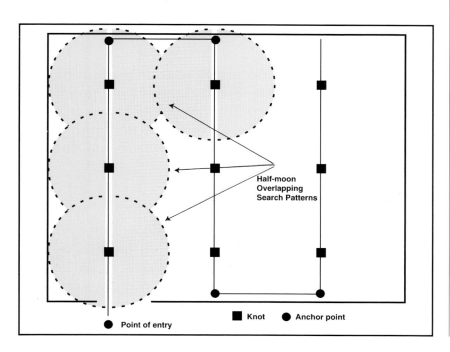

Half-moon Overlapping Search Patterns

■ Knot ● Anchor point

● Point of entry

Thermal Camera-Assisted Search

Thermal cameras give back some of the vision that smoke takes away — but not all of it! When searching for a missing firefighter, as with the other techniques, a thermal camera may help in determining the direction to take. One benefit that the other methods don't provide is the ability to see the firefighter from a distance — a distinct advantage of the camera. If a firefighter is missing and there is a thermal camera on the fireground it should be used to assist in the search — no matter what other task it may be performing!

TRAINING

Let's face it, fireground search is an important part of all fireground operations — but it's the most important part when there is a firefighter missing! How you train is how you'll perform. There's only one acceptable outcome to the search and it is tied directly to training.

Build a Solid Foundation

Continually practice basic fireground search and rescue skills. Conventional right- and left-handed search techniques, as well as all other methods, must be frequently reinforced through quality training sessions. The level of difficulty must constantly be increased during the training. Speed is critical!

Include Realistic Fireground Problems

Noise. Obstacles. Stress. No visibility. Smoke and heat (if possible). The training setting should provide anything that the fireground setting may provide. Building an effective search and rescue prop isn't difficult — it simply requires a little creativity and a lot of fireground thought. Don't hold back during training if you expect performance during an emergency. *There are no second chances on the fireground!*

PLAN THE SEARCH, SEARCH THE PLAN!

It would be great if all firefighters were equipped with integrated PASS devices, but they're not. It would be great if all firefighters turned their PASS devices on, but they don't. It would be great if all firefighters could be pinpointed on the fireground and we didn't have to expend time and effort searching for them, but they can't (economically!). ***In a true missing firefighter emergency use any and all means to locate the missing firefighter*** — Plan the Search, Search the Plan!

> **Remember,** you're looking for a firefighter! The firefighter entered the structure to perform a firefighting task (just as you would). What was the assignment? Where would the firefighter go to perform it? *Where would you have gone if given the same assignment?* Too many times we forget common sense when faced with a pressure situation — THINK, use LUNAR, move quick, have a plan and follow it!

3

ASSESSING, STABILIZING, & PACKAGING A FIREFIGHTER

Once a firefighter has been located it's important to take a minute and assess both the firefighter and the current situation. First and foremost, notify Command that the firefighter has been located! Next, after an assessment, the firefighter should be stabilized and packaged for removal. Many times by taking a few extra seconds (minutes) to stabilize and package the firefighter the overall time required to perform the rescue can be reduced.

Take a minute to make a minute, properly preparing the firefighter before you begin the rescue may mean that you won't have to stop in the middle (remember the conditions you're likely to be in) to play catch up. After the firefighter has been located remember to:

- Assess
- Stabilize
- Package

ASSESSING THE FIREFIGHTER AND THE SITUATION

When a firefighter has been located, both the firefighter and the situation should be assessed. One important step that will help lessen the overall anxiety of the situation is to *reset* the PASS device of the firefighter—if it is sounding. This action alone may drastically reduce the overall confusion of the situation.

Assessing the Firefighter

Is the firefighter conscious? Breathing? Is there air left in the firefighter's SCBA? Are there any injuries that will prevent immediate movement of the firefighter? Are there any entanglements or entrapments preventing movement? These questions must be addressed before

the firefighter can be removed.

The initial assessment of the firefighter should determine whether he is conscious and breathing and if there is adequate air in the SCBA. It may be difficult under the conditions found to determine if the firefighter is breathing but it should be attempted. If the firefighter is not breathing then immediate removal may be the only option.

Checking the status of the SCBA air supply is an important step that is often overlooked. If possible, check the cylinder valve and/or the gauge block to determine the amount of air remaining. Another simple method to determine the presence of air is to briefly break the seal of the SCBA mask (by pulling it away from the firefighter's face just enough to hear air flow). If there is air flowing then it will be heard passing through the seal.

Another assessment of the air supply should be made by listening for the low air warning device on the SCBA. If the SCBA low air alarm is sounding then it becomes critical to ensure a continuous air supply for the firefighter. An emergency air supply (see *Stabilizing the Firefighter*) should be established when the amount of air available to the firefighter is questionable.

The firefighter should also be assessed for any injuries that may prevent immediate movement. Again, the fireground conditions will have a lot to do with this assessment but, if possible, it should be done. Many times the injuries remain secondary to the consequences of not removing the firefighter immediately.

Entanglements and entrapments must also be considered. By taking the extra time to eliminate and remove any entanglements the rescue can be expedited. Rescue from a collapse situation may be as simple as lifting debris off of the firefighter or it may require a collapse team and become a complete phase of the rescue operation.

Any other factors relating to the predicament of the firefighter should be considered. Every rescue situation will be different and present different challenges. What's important is that a brief assessment of the firefighter must be conducted as soon as possible. ***Don't let the adrenaline of the event take over and force actions without thinking.***

Assessing the Fireground Conditions

An equally important part of the initial assessment involves quickly reviewing the fireground conditions. What are the current fireground conditions? Was the firefighter found in the immediate fire area or away from the fire? Are the operating crews gaining control of the fire or is it still escalating? Is your position likely to be compromised during the rescue attempt? Are additional resources needed to hold the position while you attempt to extricate the firefighter? Is flashover a possibility? Is immediate ventilation required? Is collapse a possibility? Has it already occurred? As was stated at the outset, *this is the most challenging situation you'll ever face on the fireground and the challenge may cause you to lose sight of the obvious.*

Assessing the RIT Members

One thing that's often overlooked during this initial assessment is the status of the RIT members. What's the status of each members' air supply? How long did the search take? Will the team be able to remove the downed firefighter? Once the victim has been located (maybe even before – depending on conditions) another RIT should be deployed to assist with the removal.

Assessing the Rescue/Removal Options

One additional assessment that should begin at this point is possible removal options and locations. Sure, there's still quite a bit to do before actually removing the firefighter but this little bit of preplanning will make a big difference when the rescue begins.

Is going back the way you came the best option? Is it the quickest option? Is there a closer exit?

Often times the rescue begins without considering these questions. If there's a window across the room, why not consider it? The rescue options must take into consideration all available information about the firefighter and the current working conditions. Is immediate removal required? Can the firefighter be protected in place until the situation is brought under control?

Determining the best location and method to be used to rescue the firefighter must begin as soon as the firefighter is located. This initial assessment will allow you to put additional resources in place (such as a ladder to a nearby window), if needed.

STABILIZING AND EXTRICATING THE FIREFIGHTER

Stabilizing the firefighter will depend on the firefighter's condition as well as the current operating conditions on the fireground. Does the firefighter need additional breathing air? Is a hose line required to hold back fire conditions during the rescue? Does the area need shoring due to a previous, or potential, collapse?

What about extrication? Is the firefighter trapped or pinned beneath debris? What additional equipment or

resources are needed to get the firefighter out? What about entanglement? All entanglement hazards must be removed from the firefighter so that packaging for removal can begin.

Perhaps the most important stabilizing action is that of securing the air supply of the firefighter. Once the firefighter's air supply has been secured, and depending on the current conditions, the time-sensitive nature of the rescue may be somewhat reduced.

Securing the Air Supply

Securing the air supply of the firefighter is a critical function that must be considered as soon as the firefighter is located. Consider the following questions: Does your department use personal quick-connect regulators or masks? What about surrounding departments? Is your equipment compatible with all other departments you respond with? Have you planned for incompatibilities? Have you practiced securing the air supply of a downed firefighter under realistic fireground conditions?

There are a few options available for securing the air supply of a firefighter being rescued. The option chosen is based, primarily, on the location of the firefighter and how he was found.

- Immediate removal from the environment
- Buddy breathing
- RIT Air Pack

For rescue situations involving a member of your own crew, or those when a distressed firefighter is encountered during interior operations, immediate removal or buddy breathing may be the only timely solutions. When performing as part of a rapid intervention team attaching a RIT Air Pack (or similar air supply) is the most reliable method of securing the air supply.

SCBA INCOMPATIBILITIES...

LOW PRESSURE, HIGH PRESSURE, DIFFERENT BRAND

The first step in dealing with incompatible equipment is to preplan prior to the emergency. Survey the surrounding departments and find out who has what. A couple of phone calls is all this step takes – and they're local!

The second step in dealing with this problem is familiarization. During the phone call, ask if you can borrow an SCBA so that members of your department can become familiar with it. Why is this important if you're bringing a fully-functional unit with you? This

allows you to become familiar with the unit, check out the straps and how they adjust, how the unit goes on and can be removed, and how the face piece and regulator are attached. When operating as part of a RIT, in a no visibility environment, it may be your job to secure a firefighter's air supply. That's not the time to become familiar with the equipment.

The third step is hands-on training! All firefighters should be given the assignment of securing the air supply of a downed firefighter that is using a different brand SCBA. The training should be done in no visibility conditions.

Immediate Removal from the Environment

Depending on the distance inside the building, and the proximity to an exit (window, door, safe area inside the building, etc.), one of the quickest ways to solve a low air situation is to remove the firefighter from the environment. It's critical that the firefighter can be removed immediately to fresh air, without problems, if this method is chosen. Firefighters involved in the rescue effort may not have the most accurate sense of time—this method is a tough call.

Buddy Breathing

Many of today's SCBA units are equipped with buddy-breathing capabilities. By using a buddy-breathing hose two similar SCBA units can be attached and the air supply shared. An advantage of this operation is that the air supply of the distressed firefighter is never interrupted.

A major disadvantage is that the air supply is shared and two people are now using whatever air supply was available. Two people, twice-as-fast (roughly). The RIT must find the downed firefighter(s)

before addressing air supply (that consumes air). The air remaining after performing the search, coupled with the reduced air supply of the firefighter that was found, may not provide enough air to exit the structure. Remember, searching for and then removing a downed firefighter takes a great deal of effort and increases your air consumption!

Buddy breathing may be viable for inside pairs that run into reduced air situations. It may also work in the event that a downed firefighter is found by an inside crew. The distance inside the building along with the air remaining between firefighters will determine the outcome – Command should still be notified and the RIT activated.

USING THE BUDDY BREATHING OPTION...

Securing the air supply using a buddy breathing hose will only work with the same brand SCBA that has been outfitted with the buddy breathing capability.

This option requires that the firefighter performing the rescue be proficient at connecting the buddy breath-

ing hose and ensuring there is adequate air supply, for both firefighters, to exit the area. One other consideration is the length of the buddy breathing hose. If the distance between both firefighters approaches the length of the hose then the air supply of one or both firefighters may be compromised! Keep that in mind when using this option.

RIT Air Packs

For RIT operations a complete RIT Air Pack is a much better option. By including spare SCBA units (RIT Air Packs) as part of the initial RIT equipment – a full, independent, air supply for the distressed firefighter will be brought into the building with the RIT. With this option, each RIT member's SCBA cylinder is fully available to them. An emergency has already been declared so there's no sense in handicapping the RIT before they begin by relying on their air supply to get two fire-

fighters out (the rescuer and the victim).

Complete SCBA units, with the harness and straps, can be difficult to manage during an emergency search for firefighters. Preplanning before the emergency will definitely help. Some manufacturers have come out with RIT air packages. Streamlining a few of your own air packs can provide the same result and be more cost-effective (you already own them). If you know your SCBA unit inside-and-out, like you should, then stripping it down to the bare essentials (an easy-to-carry, completely functioning unit) shouldn't be that difficult. Obviously this can't be done for every possible company so there must be a way to ensure that these RIT Air Packs are available for the RIT at the scene.

THE UNIVERSAL AIR CONNECTION (UAC)

A new feature that has been introduced into today's SCBA is a universal fitting designed to make different brands of SCBA capable of receiving air from one another. This fitting, called the "RIC Universal Air Connection (UAC)," is mandatory on all new SCBA units purchased. There are a few things that must be considered when dealing with this feature.

■ The feature is only mandatory on all newly purchased SCBA units (NFPA 1981, 2002 edition).

■ The fitting is a high pressure fitting designed to allow air from a higher pressure cylinder to be transferred to a lower pressure cylinder until both cylinders are equal in pressure.

■ The retrofit cost for older SCBA units may not be feasible for many departments.

■ If the RIT Air Pack is configured to use the UAC (a high pressure option) then it cannot–*currently*–be used for a regulator or face piece swap (low pressure). A low pressure option may be possible by using a different hose/fitting assembly—*switching is not a likely scenario under intense fireground conditions.*

■ The RIC Universal Air Connection is located directly off of the cylinder threads (where the high pressure hose attaches to the cylinder) with little flexibility. If the firefighter is trapped face-up it may not be possible to access the fitting. *In addition, if the UAC protective cover has been removed (knocked off) it can become packed with debris — which may prevent a successful connection.*

While the new fitting is a definite option it may be somewhat limiting if relied upon completely as the only method of securing the air supply.

Make sure the RIT Air Pack includes a face piece. The face piece will be needed if the firefighter is not wearing the same type of SCBA. Another possible use can occur if the firefighter has a damaged face piece.

USING THE RIT AIR PACK OPTION...

What steps need to be performed to secure the air supply of a downed firefighter using the pack you brought in? Is there enough time to strip one SCBA and place a new unit on the firefighter? Are all firefighters on the fireground using the same type of SCBA? The difficulty in securing the air supply using an SCBA brought in with the RIT depends on the type of SCBA being used by the downed firefighter.

Same Brand SCBA

If the same brand of SCBA is being used the process involves switching the downed firefighter from their air  supply to the new air supply. This may involve a complete regulator swap or a simple quick-connect hose swap. In any case, everything should be ready to go before making the exchange to reduce the amount of exposure to the environment. Once the exchange is made simply secure the RIT pack to the firefighter and remove him.

Different Brand SCBA

When the RIT encounters a different brand SCBA securing the air supply is a bit more involved. In this  case, the entire face piece will need to be swapped due to the incompatibilities. As stated above – make sure everything is ready to go before making the swap to ensure minimal exposure to the environment. The new face piece should already be attached to the RIT pack so once the swap is made simply secure the RIT pack to the firefighter and remove him.

A Few Additional Points...

■ Make sure the air supply of the RIT Air Pack is full before entering and that it's turned on before making the exchange.

■ Leave the existing SCBA in place and utilize the straps to assist in removing the firefighter.

■ Incorporate *Air Supply Secured* as one of the fire-ground benchmarks for RIT operations.

Air Supply Training Sessions

Use a vacant structure, training facility, or the apparatus bay to conduct the following RIT emergency air supply training scenarios. Scenarios should progress from familiarization to full-blown, no-visibility, rescues.

QUICK REMOVAL FROM THE ENVIRONMENT

This option has limited uses but should be included in all training sessions to avoid tunnel vision during emergency operations. Securing the air supply may be as simple as moving the firefighter to a nearby window and awaiting a ladder! Deploy a RIT to search for a downed firefighter. Place the firefighter in close proximity to a window. When the RIT finds the fire-

fighter they should secure the air supply by removing the firefighter through the window.

BUDDY BREATHING EXIT

All firefighters with buddy breathing capabilities

should be proficient at establishing buddy breathing and exiting the building. Set up a scenario where an interior crew comes across a firefighter with a low air emergency. Have a crew member establish buddy breathing and exit the building with the firefighter.

RIT AIR PACK

Deploy a RIT to search for a missing firefighter. When

the firefighter is found secure his air supply using the RIT Air Pack. Once secured, remove the firefighter from the building.

Conduct this evolution for each type of SCBA that may be encountered. Make sure to include at least one scenario that requires exchanging the face piece.

Extricating/Disentangling the Firefighter

The difficulty involved extricating and/or disentangling the firefighter depends on the situation. If the extrication is simple and can be accomplished by the immediate rescue crew (easy disentanglements, moving small amounts of debris, etc.) in a reasonable amount of time then it can be done as part of the stabilizing and packaging *(just do it and keep going)*.

If, however, the extrication will be more involved—and require additional resources, crews, or time—then treat it as a separate part of the overall rescue (covered under the Rescue Skills section).

What's important here is recognizing how entailed the extrication may be. Firefighters involved in the rescue, who fail to recognize the extent of the extrication, often exhaust themselves while trying to remove a firefighter who—until the obstruction is removed—isn't going anywhere.

A Final Thought on Stabilizing the Firefighter

Sometimes the best and quickest method of stabilizing the firefighter, *and situation,* is by just getting him out of the structure! Obviously, you don't want to cause any more damage to the firefighter but the alternative—*not making it out at all*—may be far worse.

Don't become so wrapped up in stabilizing the situation that the rescue is delayed. The actual situation encountered will determine what needs to be done. ***KEEP IT SIMPLE—secure the air, prevent further injury, and get the firefighter out!***

PACKAGING THE FIREFIGHTER

Packaging the firefighter involves getting him ready to be removed from the building. There are a few things that can be done that will assist in the overall removal. Again, KEEP IT SIMPLE!

Part of the assessment included determining possible removal locations and strategies. Is the removal location in the immediate area or does the firefighter have to be moved a long distance to the exit? Are there any stairs to deal with? Up or down? Is a ladder/window rescue required? Is it a quicker option? Do the firefighter's injuries require a backboard or stokes basket? Will a stokes basket make the removal easier? Will the current fireground conditions allow time to get a stokes or backboard? Answering these questions will help determine the packaging needed to perform the rescue.

In the simplest form, packaging the firefighter for removal will involve attaching the emergency air supply to the firefighter (so the supply is not compromised during the removal), tightening the SCBA straps so they don't loosen/slip, converting the SCBA waist strap to an improvised harness, and applying any slings, straps or rope that may be used to assist in moving the firefighter to safety.

Attaching the Emergency Air Supply to the Firefighter

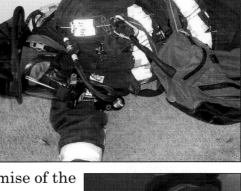

If the RIT Air Pack (or a stand-alone SCBA) is used to secure the air supply of the firefighter then the pack must be attached to the firefighter prior to moving. Failure to do this may result in a compromise of the firefighter's air supply.

A method of attaching the air supply should have been determined well in advance of the actual rescue. The pack can be clipped and/or strapped to the firefighter—what's important is that it gets done. Practice this ahead of time so when the time comes it's not forgotten.

Securing the Firefighter's SCBA Harness

The SCBA harness provides a built-in mechanism to drag a firefighter—the shoulder straps. These straps can be used to drag the firefighter and even to help carry him up or down stairs. While the harness is not a rated rescue harness it helps get the job done when it's being used as an aid.

The SCBA shoulder straps are probably the most common device used to assist in moving a downed firefighter. Before beginning the actual rescue make sure to tighten the straps as much as possible (while still allowing enough room to get a good grip). This one step will make the entire operation easier on the rescuers and more productive when it comes to moving the firefighter. **Why?** SCBA straps, no matter how tight you get them, tend to loosen over time. With the amount of movement involved in dragging a firefighter the straps will loosen and create slack allowing the SCBA to *pull away* from the firefighter. One additional step is to convert the waist strap into an improvised seat harness (see below) to prevent actually pulling the SCBA off of the firefighter. Every time the rescuers attempt to drag the firefighter the slack must be removed before any movement takes place. This extra effort causes a lot of inefficiency in the rescue effort, not to mention the fatigue and frustration to the rescuers.

The next step involves converting the SCBA waist strap to an improvised seat harness. By doing this, the SCBA is secured to the firefighter so that it isn't pulled off if the harness is used for dragging.

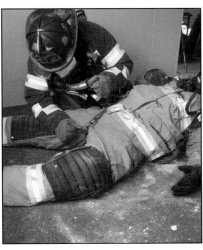

To convert the waist strap, perform these steps:

- Loosen both sides of the waist strap.

- Disconnect the waist strap buckle.

- Place the waist strap between the legs of the fire-fighter. Bring one strap from behind and one from in front so the strap is secured between the legs.

- Connect the waist strap buckle.

- Tighten the waist strap to reduce the amount of slack when pulling.

Securing Other Lifting/Moving Devices

There are a number of other pieces of equipment that are commonly used to assist in moving a firefighter. Proficiency with any of these devices must be developed before an actual rescue takes place. Other devices or aids that are commonly used include: webbing, rope, slings, backboards, stokes baskets or any other equipment that helps in moving the firefighter to safety. Often times, inexperience with the device being used actually adds to the overall rescue time. ***Don't wait for an actual rescue to try something out!***

Webbing

A simple and effective moving device is a piece of webbing. Many firefighters carry a section of 1-inch webbing (some larger) that is used to help drag a firefighter. The methods of attachment vary but the overall objective is to provide a handle that can be used to drag with. The webbing also extends the distance between the firefighter and the rescuer, which may provide more leverage to the rescuer. Depending on the method of attach-

ment, the webbing may also provide a means for two rescuers to pull/drag without interfering with each other. The length, size, and configuration of the webbing should be determined through training.

There are a number of variations used to apply the webbing that is used to assist in moving a firefighter. One method involves wrapping the webbing in front of the firefighter's chest and under the arms. The webbing is fed around the chest and under the arms and used—from behind the firefighter—as a handle to drag with. Another common method involves looping the webbing under the shoulder straps of the SCBA. The webbing is then extended behind the firefighter and used as a handle.

SLINGS

There are also a few commercial slings that can be used to assist in moving a firefighter. These devices have been developed to help make it easier to move a firefighter. One particular device, the Sling-Link MAST™, is a series of five sewn loops. The Sling-Link

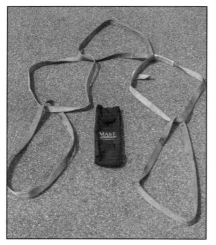 

can be applied in a variety of ways to assist in moving a firefighter. An extra advantage of the Sling-Link MAST™ is that it's a rated lifting device.

ROPE

Rope can also be used in a variety of ways when it comes to moving a firefighter. Many times it's applied the same as webbing and used as a handle to help drag a firefighter. Other  times it is clipped to the firefighter and used—from a distance—to pull the firefighter out.

What's important, with the use of rope, webbing or a sling, is that it not be looped around the chest in such a way that it restricts the firefighter's breathing when it is tightened.

STOKES BASKET/BACKBOARD

Depending on the circumstances (injuries), or removal distance, the firefighter may be placed in a stokes basket or on a backboard. When using either of these devices just make sure to secure the firefighter correctly at the beginning. These devices can be carried, if conditions permit, or slid across the floor to make the removal a bit easier.

Remember, it's important that all members are on the same page when it comes to any devices used to aid in the rescue. Much confusion—which equates to delay in the overall rescue—can result from an unfamiliar device being thrown into the mix at the wrong time. Train!

4

FIREFIGHTER RESCUE AND REMOVAL TECHNIQUES

There's no way to tell what type of rescue situation will be encountered—or how it will have to be handled—until the firefighter is located. Once the firefighter has been located and stabilized it's time to concentrate on the rescue and removal.

If a firefighter is trapped, and requires some type of extrication, but conditions are so severe that you can't operate the equipment needed to perform the extrication (saws, spreaders...) then the only option may be to protect the firefighter while other crews work to improve the overall conditions. Remember, part of the overall rescue involves preventing further injury to the firefighter—protecting the firefighter in place may be required.

There are a number of rescue skills that may be involved in moving a firefighter from the location found to safety. These skills may include any combination of the following:

■ Extrication from collapse/Disentanglement

■ Drags and/or carries

■ Removal through a wall breach

■ Movement up or down stairs

■ Window rescues

■ Rescue from below (through a floor...)

■ Other rescue situations...

Developing proficiency with each individual type of rescue skill will aid tremendously when faced with a difficult rescue on the fireground. During most rescues it takes a few of these skills, combined, to actually get the job done and the firefighter to safety.

EXTRICATION FROM COLLAPSE/DISENTANGLEMENT

Removal from an entrapment or entanglement may be as simple as lifting debris or cutting a few wires/cables. On the other hand, removal may require the equipment and expertise of a complete collapse rescue unit. It's critical that the rescue team sees the *big picture* when it comes to extricating the fire-fighter. A failure to assess the overall problem—by focusing strictly on a smaller (specific) part of it—will create tunnel vision, cause frustration and exhaustion,

and may ultimately cause the rescue to fail. Essentially, the rescue team becomes a part of the problem.

As we discussed earlier, a simple entrapment or entanglement—that can be handled quickly by the initial rescue team—will usually be taken care of during the stabilizing/packaging phase of the rescue. For more advanced entrapments, additional equipment, personnel and time may be required.

Many rescues are a result of a collapse that has trapped one or more firefighters. The extrication may require the removal of both surface (plaster, sheetrock, ceiling tiles…) and structural (lathe, ceiling/floor assemblies, walls…) material.

This removal may have to take place under extreme fireground conditions—requiring the use of additional companies (and hose lines) to protect the rescue team while they operate.

Protection of the trapped firefighter(s) is a critical step that must be performed while the extrication is being completed.

Tools that may be required include: cutting and prying tools (saws, axes, sledges, pry bars, ladders...) and/or lifting and spreading tools (air bags, porta-powers, hydraulic or battery operated spreaders...). Any other tools that may be used to free the trapped firefighter(s) should be called for, and staged, as soon as possible.

Finding and stabilizing the firefighter(s) may be the only RAPID part of this rescue. If the removal becomes an extended event then make sure to have plenty of personnel on hand.

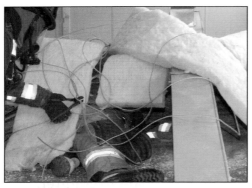

A serious entanglement may result from a partial ceiling collapse. There are a tremendous amount of wires, cables, and other entanglement hazards found above today's ceilings. HVAC ductwork, computer wires, cable TV wires—*who knows what else*—are all potential firefighter killers. Removing a firefighter from this type of entanglement must be done in a systematic fashion. When any part of the entanglement hazard is removed it must be moved away from the immediate area so that it doesn't become an additional hazard at a later point. Preplan your exit route and make sure not to place the debris anywhere near this route.

When dealing with larger collapse situations (such as a complete floor) with firefighters trapped it's important to call for help early. A collapse rescue team may be required for both equipment and expertise. Secondary collapse should always be considered. Lifting and shoring of the collapsed area may be required before the firefighter(s) can be removed.

Realistic training is a must when it comes to removing a firefighter from any type of collapse, entrapment, or entanglement. The ability to deal with both the entrapment and the fireground conditions (heat, no-visibility, noise, confusion, active fire...) makes this one of the most difficult rescue situations found.

DRAGS AND CARRIES

Moving a firefighter any distance on the fireground usually involves some type of drag and/or carry. Carries—in the truest sense—are limited by the fireground conditions and the weight of the firefighter. It's not that easy to actually pick up and move a firefighter (no matter how many people are available) when visibility is near zero and heat is keeping you close to the ground. Drags are a much more common method of moving a firefighter.

Communication During Lifts and Drags

Communication is critical when performing firefighter rescues. Miscommunication quickly leads to frustration and exhaustion. Too much communication slows the rescue and consumes additional breathing air. Consider using either **"READY—DRAG,"** or **"READY—LIFT"** during rescue operations. Pausing after **"READY"** gives the other rescuers a chance to say **"NO"** if they're not ready.

Carries

When it is possible to carry a downed firefighter, any of the basic carries can be used. Whatever works! If a stokes basket or backboard are available they can be used to make the carry easier.

One improvised carry technique creates a litter out of two pike poles (or something similar). If time permits and a carry is going to be used, consider this technique. The pike poles are placed on each side of the victim and woven through the SCBA straps. Thread the pike pole under the shoulder strap, under the waist strap *(difficult if a harness conversion was made)* and along the side of the victim's thigh. Place the victims calf up and over the pike pole. Place the pike pole on the opposite side the same way.

Once the pike poles are in position, two firefighters can drag the litter or two or more firefighters can pick it up and carry it.

Drags

When preparing to drag a downed firefighter a number of things should be considered. How far will the firefighter have to be moved? How many firefighters are able to assist? Does space permit the extra help? Are there any obstacles that must be considered? What are the current fireground conditions and how will they affect your ability to drag the firefighter? *As with all rescue skills—have a plan before you begin!*

ONE FIREFIGHTER DRAGS

The type of drag will depend on the number of firefighters available to help. When only one firefighter is available then drag the firefighter however you can. There's not much else to say here except use whatever technique works best to get the job done. Some tech-

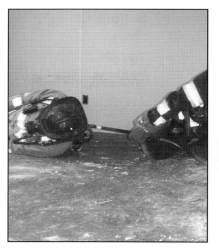 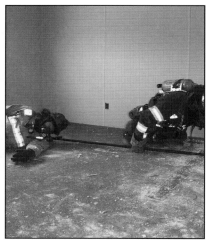

niques that may work include: using the SCBA shoulder straps, using a piece of webbing or rope, using a sling, tool or whatever else may be available.

TWO FIREFIGHTER DRAGS

When it comes to dragging a downed firefighter, two firefighters are definitely better than one! When there are two firefighters available, and they work together as a team, a downed firefighter can be moved a considerable distance.

One method that works well has one firefighter dragging the SCBA shoulder straps (or another device) while the second firefighter pushes. After tightening all of the SCBA straps, the firefighter at the head grasps the shoulder straps while the second firefighter kneels at the feet of

the downed firefighter. Once in position, the second firefighter raises one leg of the downed firefighter over his shoulder and leans against the back of the downed firefighters leg (hamstring area). The dragging firefighter can move backwards or turn and use one arm to pull while facing the direction of the move.

When ready, the two firefighters work as a team and—upon the call ("READY–DRAG") of the firefighter at the head position—simultaneously drag and push the firefighter. This method distributes the work load between the two firefighters and allows the downed firefighter to be moved a considerable distance.

Another method that may work—if conditions and space allow—is to have both firefighters positioned at the head dragging. Each rescuer grasps one of the SCBA shoulder straps and drags in the intended direction. One problem that may arise when using the SCBA shoulder straps is that both rescuers may have difficulty getting a strong pull due to their being so close together. A solution to this is to use  either a sling or a piece of rope/webbing to extend the distance between both the rescuers and the downed firefighter. This increased distance allows the rescuers to get better leverage while dragging. Training ahead of time, again, is the key to success.

If three rescuers are available then a combination drag/push—with one rescuer pushing and two dragging—seems to work best. If more rescuers are available the best option may be to use two or three to drag the downed firefighter for a distance while the others lead the way out. Before the first set of rescuers become exhausted they should switch positions with the others. Too many rescuers trying to drag at one time may actually slow the entire operation down.

RESCUE THROUGH A WALL BREACH

Wall breaching during firefighter rescue may be required, either to access and remove the firefighter or to create an exit during a rescue. When collapse has occurred, or when no other access to the victim is available, a wall breach may have to be performed. When moving a firefighter to safety the escape route may or may not follow an existing path. One removal option—when no others are available or when conditions require drastic measures—may be to breach a wall, move the firefighter through the breach, and continue with the rescue.

Wall breaching, as an individual firefighter survival technique, was discussed in *Firefighter Survival*. The actual breaching technique used during a firefighter rescue is the same (see inset). Once the breach is created, and the conditions are deemed acceptable on the other side, the downed firefighter can be moved through the opening.

Moving the downed firefighter through the breach is essentially an extension of the drag. **With one rescuer**—position the downed firefighter

as close to the breach as possible. Once through the breach reach back and grasp the SCBA straps of the firefighter and pull him through. The bigger the breach in the wall—the better. Once through the breach the rescue can continue.

BREACHING A WALL

When breaching a wall to access and rescue a downed firefighter, choose a location to breach and use a tool to break through the wall. Obviously, breaching frame construction will be much easier than block or concrete construction. Penetrate all the way through the wall to ensure that there's nothing blocking the

other side (failure to check the other side will result in a lot of wasted energy if an obstacle is encountered).

Once the opening is large enough to get through (with frame construction you may be able to move a stud out of the way by striking it with your tool) remove any potential entanglement hazards. *Take the time to make the opening larger than you normally would for an individual escape—you'll need a bit more room to get the downed firefighter through.*

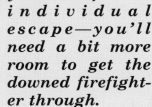

Lastly, check both the integrity of the floor and the environment on the other side of the opening and make your way through. *Getting through the opening may require a reduced profile maneuver with your SCBA and/or the SCBA of the victim.*

With two or more firefighters performing the rescue it's simply a matter of positioning so there's rescuers on both sides of the opening. The movement of the downed firefighter is the same.

MOVEMENT UP OR DOWN STAIRS

Moving a firefighter up or down a flight of stairs definitely requires technique. While moving down a flight of stairs is a bit easier it still requires coordination, communication and teamwork.

Moving a Firefighter Up a Flight of Stairs

Moving a firefighter up a flight of stairs is exhausting! Muscle alone may not get it done. In fact, the right technique makes a huge difference. When faced with moving a firefighter up a flight of stairs, remember:

■ Move one or two steps at a time.

■ Control your breathing.

■ Size up the conditions before beginning—*don't want to get caught halfway up.*

■ The SCBA cylinder is one of the most common obstructions that must be overcome when moving a firefighter up a flight of stairs. *Recognize the obstruction and THINK through it—frustration and exhaustion will take over if you don't!*

When two firefighters are available to move a downed firefighter up a flight of stairs, position firefighter one on the stairs—ready to use the downed firefighter's SCBA straps to lift—and firefighter two at the base of the stairs. Once the downed firefighter is moved into position—seated with his back towards the stairs—the move up the stairs can begin.

The lift begins by having firefighter one lift the downed firefighter (victim) up the first couple of stairs by using the SCBA straps, this puts the victim in position so that firefighter two can begin to assist. *Firefighter two can also assist with the initial lift by using the victim's legs.*

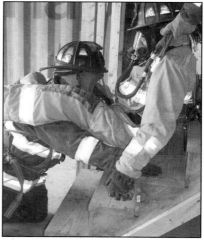

Once the victim is in position on the stairs, firefighter two can get into position for the actual lift. Firefighter two places the legs of the victim over his shoulders—so that he can use his legs to lift the victim. When both rescuers are ready to proceed firefighter one calls for the lift ("READY—LIFT", pausing after "READY" to allow the other rescuer to say "NO"). Firefighter one lifts/pulls up using the victim's SCBA straps while firefighter two pushes/lifts the victim from below. Part of firefighter two's lifting action must include pulling the victim *away* from the stairs. This is important to prevent the SCBA cylinder from getting caught on each stair tread during the lift. Failure to prevent the

SCBA from *hanging up* will quickly tire—and frustrate—both rescuers.

Another variation of this lift—which may provide a smoother movement up the stairs—uses one SCBA strap (firefighter one) and one leg (firefighter two) while rotating the victim slightly to one

side so that the SCBA cylinder is not riding directly on the stair treads. This method also seems to give firefighter two more control over the push/lift—*especially the ability to keep the victim and SCBA elevated slightly off of the stairs.*

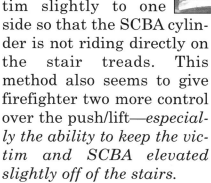

One other technique (which is set up the same way) involves actually carrying the victim up the

stairs. Firefighter one places his arms under the arms of the victim and locks his hands. Firefighter two positions as before. On the call of firefighter one, the victim is lifted up off of the stairs and carried up. While this  requires a bit more strength it may actually be easier than the other methods.

With any of the techniques, the speed of the overall move up the stairs is controlled by firefighter one. It's important that firefighter two doesn't overpower firefighter one during the lift. This simply wears out both firefighters and makes for a longer, inefficient, movement.

With three rescuers—as with dragging a downed firefighter—position two at the head of the victim (on the stairs) to lift the SCBA straps and one at the victim's feet to push/lift. The size of the staircase plays a big role in how many rescuers can actually help in the lifting portion of the rescue. If the staircase is only big enough for one firefighter at the victim's head then consider switching off during the lift to reduce fatigue. *The objective is to get the victim up the stairs and have enough energy left to continue with the rescue*—share the workload!

During the lift up the stairs use anything available to assist. Railings can be used to help pull yourself up. Landings can be used to briefly pause/rest or to reposition or switch rescuers. Remember, the firefighter one position will have a heavy workload so make sure to swap off during the lift—if possible.

If time permits, a backboard or stokes basket may allow you to slide the victim up the stairs. This option may not always work (or make things easier) but it should be considered. A rope may also be attached to the head of the device and pulled (by additional rescuers) from the top of the stairs.

The bottom line is that moving a firefighter up a flight of stairs will wear the rescuers out—*no matter what kind of shape they're in!* Training on these skills should be done ahead of time—with as many variations as possible—so you'll be able to adapt and overcome problems that may arise during an actual rescue.

Moving a Firefighter Down a Flight of Stairs

Moving a firefighter down a flight of stairs—while still a difficult task—is much easier than going up. One of the biggest challenges with this skill is slowing down enough to prevent further injuries to the downed firefighter.

The easiest way to move a firefighter down a flight of stairs is to drag the firefighter, head first (rotated slightly to one side), using the SCBA shoulder straps or grasping him under the arms. The technique also protects the head and neck of the firefighter being removed. When two rescuers are available, one drags the victim while the second acts as a guide.

The victim should be moved into position at the top of the stairs. Once in position, firefighter two (guide) moves down a few steps—clearing any debris—to get into position to guide firefighter one (drag). The firefighter performing the drag moves down a step or two, grasps the victim's SCBA straps and begins to drag him

down the stairs (moving backwards down the steps). The feet of the victim are unsupported and drop down the stairs one step at a time. During the drag the guide firefighter makes sure the stairs are free of debris and that the path below remains clear of other personnel. The guide also acts as a support for the firefighter performing the drag—to prevent a fall.

There are a number of other ways that a downed firefighter can be moved down a flight of stairs—some rougher than others. What's important is that you practice a number of different techniques beforehand and you try and prevent further injury to the downed firefighter during the actual emergency.

WINDOW RESCUES

Removing a downed firefighter through a window is much harder than it appears. To complete this type of rescue you have to find the victim, find and clear a window, and get the victim out the window to safety. For first floor window rescues the firefighter can be removed by awaiting firefighters and brought directly to on-scene medical crews. For upper floor window rescues, the firefighter must first be moved to the ground—which is no simple task—before being brought to medical crews.

While a window rescue should not be the first choice, when it comes to removing a downed firefighter, it may be the only choice due to fireground conditions. If a firefighter is located with a window nearby, the advantages of immediate removal through the window may outweigh any other removal options.

When deciding if a window rescue should be performed, consider the following questions:

■ Is there a window nearby that can be used?

■ Has the window been cleared and—if dealing with an upper floor rescue—is there a ladder present?

■ Is there an easier way? Will time allow another option?

Once it's decided that the firefighter will be removed through a window—get to the window, prepare it if necessary, move the firefighter into the window, and get him out and to safety.

Before talking about actual window rescues it's important to discuss clearing windows.

Clearing a Window

When a window will be used to perform a rescue it should be cleared out completely. Clearing a window involves removing all of the glass, the rails and sash, and any accessories in or around the window (screens, blinds, shades, curtains...). As the saying goes—*make the window a door!* Failure to take the few extra seconds needed to completely clear the window could result in a delayed—or failed—rescue.

The window can be cleared by a member of the inside rescue team or a member of the RIT performing proactive fireground tasks during the fireground operation (see Part II: RIT).

Enlarging Window Openings

One technique that may be performed to assist with window rescues involves enlarging the opening being used for removal. This technique is used on wood-frame structures (and possibly lightweight metal structures) that can be cut away with a power saw. While the technique is primarily used for first floor windows, it may be possible to perform this procedure on upper floor windows as well. The difficulty in performing the cut and enlarging the opening must be weighed against other possible removal options.

There are two common techniques used to enlarge the window opening for removal. One technique involves removing the area between the window sill and the floor. The second involves taking the above section (beneath the sill) plus an adjacent section of the wall beneath the window. The method to be used should be decided before beginning the cutting operations so that extra cuts are not made.

Removing the Wall Beneath the Window Sill

Removing the area below the sill (basically cutting the window down to the floor) eliminates the need to lift the firefighter up and over the sill. The lift is, by far, the hardest part of the removal for the inside firefighters.

To remove the sill a chain saw is used to extend the window all the way down to the floor. Two cuts are made, one on each side of the window, from the sill to the floor. A third cut is then made across the floor line— connecting the first two cuts. The sill area can then be removed which leaves a door-sized opening in the exterior wall.

It's important to keep everyone clear of the cut area when the chain saw is operating and to ensure the power has been cut—eliminating the chance of cutting through a live wire during the procedure.

Removing a Larger Wall Section Below the Window Sill

When removing a larger section of the wall beneath the window sill, the cutting procedure is a little different. The window is extended to the floor on one side by making a vertical cut from the sill to the floor. On the opposite side (which was also cut straight down when removing the sill) a horizontal cut is made perpendicular to the window—going away from it. This will make the size of the opening beneath the window wider. After cutting out the desired distance another vertical cut is made (from the top of the horizontal cut) down to the floor line. A final cut joins both vertical cuts and the wall section is removed. This opening would allow a firefighter to be rolled out from the inside.

Again, as with the sill removal, it's important to make sure everyone is clear of the cutting area and that the power has been cut.

Types of Window Rescues

- First floor window rescues

- Upper floor window rescues with ground ladders

- Rope-assisted upper floor window rescues with ground ladders

- Upper floor window rescues with aerials/towers

- The Denver Drill

First Floor Window Rescues

Removing a firefighter from a first floor window is something that should be considered any time a downed firefighter is located on the first floor of a structure. Many times, a few extra seconds of searching by a member of the rescue team—*after the firefighter has been found*—would allow for a quicker removal through a nearby window, solving many of the immediate problems created by the fireground conditions.

Rescue through a first floor window involves clearing the window, notifying Command of the window location so that additional personnel can help from the outside, lifting the firefighter into the window and moving him to safety.

There are a number of ways the firefighter can be lifted up and through the window. The method used often depends on how the downed firefighter has been positioned at the window. A little planning while dragging the firefighter to the window can help set up the lift—which is critical when dealing with upper floor ladder rescues. When dealing with first floor window rescues the positioning is not as critical because the firefighters who are helping from the outside are able to stand on

the ground—eliminating any of the problems associated with carrying the firefighter down the ladder.

The easiest way to lift a firefighter up and out of a first floor window is to lift the firefighter head-first, face-up. This method allows the inside rescuer(s) to lift the firefighter up into the window and rest his body on the window sill (this is the natural sitting position of the body). Once the firefighter is resting on the window sill the inside and outside rescuer(s) can reposition. The outside rescuer(s) can grab the SCBA shoulder straps of the firefighter and begin pulling him out while the inside rescuer(s) guides the legs and feet of the firefighter up and over the window sill.

Other lifts may include head-first, face-down and feet-first-face-up. Whichever lift is used the objective remains the same—get the firefighter out of the area and to safety without causing additional injury.

Upper Floor Window Rescues with Ground Ladders

Upper floor window rescues are a bit more difficult than first floor rescues because the victim must be moved down to the ground.

When dealing with upper floor window rescues that involve the use of ground ladders one additional step must be added—*a ground ladder must be properly placed and positioned.*

LADDER PLACEMENT

Ladder Angle

While traditional fireground ladder placement teaches you to place ground ladders at the proper climbing angle (75°, 1/4 of the distance...), ladders used for emergency escape or firefighter rescue should  be placed at a lesser angle. A lesser angle allows the weight of the downed firefighter to be carried more by the ladder—rather than the rescuer. This angle also places the rescuer in a more favorable position—allowing him to lean into the ladder if problems begin to develop. With the traditional angle the firefighter is more upright which creates a tendency to lean backwards when carrying the victim down.

Ladder Tip

The tip of the ladder should be placed at, or slightly below, the window sill. Placing the ladder tip at this location reduces the chance of the victim getting hung up while being lifted out through the window. This position also allows the entire window (if interior conditions allow) to be used during the rescue.

The ladder may also be positioned above the window if a high-point pulley or mechanical advantage system will be used. This placement is done when performing a rope-assisted ladder rescue (see Rope-Assisted Ladder Rescues).

Ground Ladder Rescues

There are a number of ways that a firefighter can be lifted into a window and carried down a ladder. In a true emergency, prior training—by all members involved in the rescue—will pay great dividends. How the firefighter is handed out the window dictates how he will be carried down the ladder (head-first, feet-first, facing the ladder, back towards the ladder). If the rescuers performing the lift from the inside aren't on the same page as the rescuer(s) who will be carrying the victim down (or vice-versa) there's a real possibility that the victim could be dropped.

Upper floor window rescues should be looked at from two sides—inside and outside. The inside rescuers have to get the victim to the window and then lift him up and out, to the rescuer on the ladder. The outside rescuer(s) must properly position to receive the victim and then safely lower him to the ground. During these types of rescues, a little planning by the inside rescuers—when positioning the firefighter at the window sill—will make the entire rescue go a lot smoother. *It sounds a lot easier than it is!*

For the ladder rescue described here there are at least two rescuers inside and the victim is facing the ladder as he is carried down by the rescuer. This method provides the rescuer with a great deal of control, reduces the direct weight on the rescuer, and provides a quick and easy way to stop and hold the victim in place—if something starts to go wrong.

If only one rescuer is available inside the window then he will have to do *whatever it takes* to get the firefighter into the window.

The Inside Team

As stated earlier, a little planning by the inside team—before reaching the window and actually lifting the victim—can make this type of rescue a whole lot easier. The team should determine, ahead of time, how the victim will be lifted up and out and who will take the lead when communicating at the window. Communicating with the rescuer on the ladder is a big part of any ladder rescue.

POSITIONING THE DOWNED FIREFIGHTER

The firefighter is positioned face-down, with his feet at the window sill (head pointing away) to perform this rescue. This places the lightest part of the victim (legs) out the window first — allowing the outside rescuer to gradually accept the full weight of the victim. It also prevents the victim from having to be *flipped over* on the window sill — which would be required if he was lifted face up. To reduce the overall effort during the lift the victim's knees can be bent and his feet rested on the window sill. This little extra effort helps reduce the possibility of the feet getting caught against the wall or at the window sill while lifting. It also brings the victim a little closer to the window *(every little bit helps)*.

LIFTING THE DOWNED FIREFIGHTER

Once the victim is in position the inside team should check with the rescuer on the ladder to make sure he is ready to proceed and that everyone knows how the victim will be handed out.

When lifting the victim it's important to lift together. One of the most common problems that occurs when lifting a firefighter through a window is that the rescuers aren't lifting at the same time. This just adds to the frustration levels and makes it even more exhausting.

To lift the victim the inside rescuers should position on both sides, facing each other. The easiest way to lift the torso is to grasp the SCBA shoulder straps (or the harness itself). Lifting the legs is a bit more difficult because there's nothing easy to grab. An easy way to lift the legs together—which requires some practice ahead of time—is for both rescuers to reach under the victim's legs (somewhere under the thighs) and

lock hands. This creates a solid lifting point and allows both legs to be lifted at the same time.

Once the rescuers are set to lift, and the rescuer on the ladder is ready, they can lift the victim up and move him into the window. The victim's thighs can be rested on the window sill and his torso on the rescuers legs while they reposition to finish handing him out.

The Outside Team

The rescuer on the ladder should receive the victim by guiding the victim's legs to the outside of the ladder rails and positioning one arm through the crotch of the victim—locking his hand behind the rail. The rescuer's sec-

ond hand should be locked behind the opposite rail so the victim's torso can be lowered onto his arm. The victim is carried at an angle across the ladder. The angle can be adjusted to help control the victim as he is slid down the ladder.

If problems develop (victim starts sliding too far to one side, rescuers hands start to slip, fatigue...) the rescuer can just lean into the ladder. This squeezes the victim between the rescuer and the ladder and holds him in place. The rescuer can then readjust, as needed, solve the problem and continue the rescue.

Anything on the front or sides of the victim (tools, spanner belt, flashlight...) may get hung up on the rungs of the ladder as the victim is slid down. If possible and time permits, these items should be removed prior to handing the victim out the window.

Other Ladder Rescue Variations

There are a number of other ladder carries taught and used. The method used should be practiced ahead of time so that you know what to expect. Even though one method is agreed upon—the chaos of the entire rescue event results in even the best plans going off course—another method may have to be used. Training will bring out many of the potential problems that may arise during an actual rescue (SCBA hanging up on ladder rungs, etc.).

One carry that is used requires the victim's SCBA to be removed prior to lifting him out onto the ladder. In this carry, the victim is handed out face-up and feet first. The victim's legs are placed over the shoulders of the rescuer and the victim is slid down with his back against the ladder. This carry tends to push the rescuer away from the ladder, increasing the chances of the rescuer falling backward.

A head-first carry may be required because of interior conditions or victim positioning. If the victim is handed out the window face-down and head-first then the outside rescuer will have to do whatever it takes to get the victim down the ladder safely.

The bottom line is to practice as many variations as possible so that you're able to adapt to the situation and get the job done!

MULTIPLE GROUND LADDERS

If time permits or the size or condition of the victim requires multiple rescuers, two or more ladders can be set side-by-side to perform a window rescue. The benefit of multiple ladders is that the victim can be laid across all of them (distributing the weight across them) and multiple rescuers can be used to help carry the victim to the ground.

When using multiple ladders it's important to set them all at the same height and angle, and as close together as possible. If the ladders are not set the same they may actually cause more harm than good.

Rope-Assisted Ladder Rescues

A rope-assisted ladder rescue is also an option. This rescue requires some additional equipment (rope, pulleys), and a slightly different ladder position, but it may come in handy when there aren't enough rescuers.

HIGH-POINT PULLEY

The **high-point pulley** system is an easy system to set up and use. To perform this type of rescue the ladder must be positioned above the top of the window (not at or below the sill like the other rescues). This placement allows a pulley to be set at a *high-point* above the victim's position.

Once the pulley is set, a life-safety rope is rigged through the pulley—with one end going to the victim and the other down the underside of the ladder to the ground. At the ground, the rope is brought under a rung and extended out in front of the ladder. The rung provides friction to assist in lowering the firefighter (weaving the rope through multiple rungs increases the friction). Firefighters on the ground grab the rope and perform the lowering.

The rope is clipped to the victim with a carabiner. While the SCBA harness is a logical attachment point it is not a rated lowering harness or device. If this system is used, a sling (or webbing/rope) or lowering harness should be applied to the victim and attached to the rope.

The victim is then positioned in the window by the rescuers. The rope can also be used to assist the lift. Once the victim is in place on the window sill the slack in the rope is taken up and the victim's weight is slowly lowered onto the rope. The

firefighter's on the ground then lower the firefighter.

TWO-TO-ONE HIGH-POINT MECHANICAL ADVANTAGE

Another rope-assisted ladder rescue that can be used creates a two-to-one mechanical advantage by placing an additional pulley on the victim.

The rope comes from the bottom of the ladder (the same as the previous description) and runs up the back side of the ladder and through the high-point pulley. *Here's the variation*—the rope then proceeds down to the victim, through a pulley attached to the victim (this is where just the rope was attached before) and then back up to the ladder. This two-to-one system may provide the extra muscle needed to lift the victim up and out of the window—making it easier to get the job done.

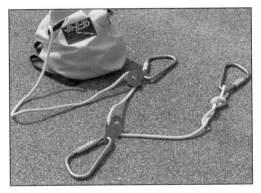

It is essential for all members to train with rope-assisted ladder rescues before

putting them to use on the fireground. The systems require a team effort and all members of the team must be on the same page to ensure success.

Aerial-Assisted Ladder Rescues

For windows that are above the reach of ground ladders it may be possible to use an aerial ladder or platform to perform the rescue.

For those departments that don't have an aerial, consider establishing mutual-aid agreements for their use during normal fireground operations as well as during possible rescue situations.

When considering the use of an aerial device, ask:

- Is there access to the area that will allow the apparatus to be set up?

- Will the aerial/platform reach the window to be used for the rescue?

- Is there a competent operator available? *In many departments, if the aerial is not used at the outset then the operator becomes part of an inside or outside truck team—taking him away from the apparatus.*

Training is critical—before the emergency—on all aspects of the aerial- or tower-assisted rescue. Rescue teams should practice different techniques at assisting and/or carrying a victim down an aerial ladder. Teams should also practice on the best techniques to move a victim to the ground using a tower ladder or platform.

The Denver Drill

A specific window rescue technique used to remove a downed firefighter, developed as a direct result of a firefighter fatality, is known as the Denver Drill. Engineer Mark Langvardt of the Denver Fire Department died in the line of duty on September 28, 1992, while operating at a 2-story commercial building. Due to the circumstances, firefighters were unable to perform a window rescue from the exterior and, after an extended period of time due to the ongoing fire, finally had to breach an interior block wall to complete the rescue.

The window rescue was complicated by the positioning of the victim, the building, and the fire. The victim was found face down with his head up against the wall below the window. The room where Engineer Langvardt was found was a file room. File cabinets lined both sides of the room leaving only a 28-inch wide aisle. The window was small (only 20-inches wide) and set high in the wall (42-inch sill height). Adding to the difficulty was the fact that the floor partially collapsed (due to the ongoing fire) making it impossible for rescue crews to reach the victim from the interior. The firefighting efforts were ongoing during the entire rescue.

The Denver Drill is a technique where two firefighters enter the window, position the victim for removal, and lift him up and—with the help of the outside rescuer(s)—out of the window. This technique is extremely difficult in training sessions so you can imagine what it would be like under intense fireground conditions like those found in Denver.

PERFORMING THE DENVER DRILL

Firefighter one enters the window over the top of the victim, moves away from the wall to the feet of the victim and turns to face the window. Once in position, he rotates the victim onto his back and places him in a sitting position. Firefighter one then tightens the SCBA shoulder straps of the victim.

Next, firefighter two enters the window and positions himself between the wall and the victim.

Firefighter two then moves back towards the window until his SCBA is resting against the wall. The victim is then slid back (in a seated position) to firefighter two. *At this point, fire-*

fighter two is in position to lift.

Next, firefighter one pulls the victim towards himself, lifting him up off the ground, so that firefighter two can position his knees up and under the victim.

Firefighter one—in a kneeling position—then leans forward between the crotch of the victim and places both of the victims legs over his shoulders. *Both firefighters are now ready to lift the victim up and out of the window.*

With the outside rescuers in position and ready to assist, the insider rescuers—under the control of firefighter one—prepare to lift. Simultaneously, firefighter two lifts/presses the victim up using the SCBA harness/cylinder as firefighter one squats the victim up using his legs. It's important for firefighter one to pull back slightly during the lift so the victim isn't folded together and so that firefighter two isn't crushed against the wall. As the inside firefighters are lifting, the outside firefighter(s) can assist by lifting up on the SCBA shoulder straps.

During the lift, if either rescuer needs to reposition and get another grip, fire-fighter two can reposition his knees and rest the victim on them. When both rescuers are ready the lift can continue.

Once the victim is on the window sill he can be repositioned so the outside rescuer(s) can complete the rescue.

DENVER DRILL TRAINING SESSIONS

A Denver Drill prop is inexpensive and easy to construct. Most training sessions progress from no SCBA on the rescuers to full-blown scenarios involving smoke. The prop is usually constructed on ground level. For advanced training sessions, incorporate an upper floor

Denver Drill prop that requires the use of a ground ladder for final victim removal.

The dimensions for a Denver Drill prop are as follows:

- 20-inch wide window
- 42-inch high window sill
- 28-inch wide aisle (work area)
- 8-foot deep aisle (work area)
- 4-foot high aisle walls
  Higher walls work and add to the difficulty!

RESCUES FROM BELOW

A firefighter who has fallen through a floor – or through a roof – presents a very challenging rescue situation for members of his crew, and/or members of a rescue team. For success, the firefighter must be protected from the surrounding conditions, protected from further injury, and removed to safety — *all easier said than done!*

There are a number of reasons that a firefighter may fall through a floor – to a lower level – including: fire-weakened floors, missing or burned-out stairs, interior collapse, or intentional holes cut to keep others out (arsonists, drug houses, etc.). Firefighters may also fall through a weakened roof deck or roof assembly while performing roof top operations. Whatever the case may be, a firefighter that falls through a hole to a lower level will require immediate assistance to prevent further injury.

Any firefighter who falls through a floor to a lower level should immediately attempt self-rescue. A critical step in any self-rescue situation is notifying others that you are in trouble (MAY-DAY). In addition, attempting to gain composure and beginning a systematic troubleshooting process to solve your problem should begin immediately.

In many instances, the firefighter who has fallen through an opening, to a lower level, will be unable to assist in his own rescue. Whether due to injury, entanglement, entrapment due to collapse debris, or fire conditions in the immediate area, the downed firefighter may be unable to attempt self-rescue. More importantly, the firefighter may be incapacitated, or unconscious, and unable to assist others who are attempting to perform the rescue. When approaching the area of the downed firefighter, rescue teams should consider all possibilities—and resource needs—before proceeding.

Stabilizing the Rescue Area

It's important for the rescuer(s) to anticipate additional problems in the area where the firefighter has fallen through. Whether from a burn-through or a collapse, the structure has already failed and further failure is likely and should be anticipated.

The area around where the firefighter fell through should be stabilized to prevent further collapse from the weight of the rescuers. Use whatever is available in the immediate area (doors, shelves, etc.) to distribute the weight of the rescuers that must work in close proximity to the actual opening or collapse.

When access has been gained to the victim (see below) the area directly around the victim should be shored – if immediate removal is not possible – by moving furniture or other large objects close to the victim to support any additional collapse from above.

Accessing the Firefighter

One of the immediate concerns, once the actual location of the firefighter has been determined, is gaining access to the firefighter in order to assess his condition, establish an emergency air supply, and protect him from surrounding fireground conditions (if needed).

There are two possible ways to access the firefighter: from above or from an access point on the lower level. The quickest route should be used.

If there is a known access point on the same level as the firefighter, and it can be used without any delay, then it would be the logical choice. If there is no access from below, or there is concern that the route might be delayed, then a rescuer should gain access from above (it is wise to attempt both methods simultaneously).

When gaining access from above, a rescuer can lower himself into the area, be lowered by rescuers using a safety line or hose line, or climb down a ladder (if available).

Whichever method is chosen, remember that the area is already compro-

mised so any excess impact may cause more damage to the structure—or injury to the downed firefighter.

One other possibility that exists is that immediate access to the firefighter cannot be accomplished. If this is the case it may be necessary for the rescuer(s) to protect the downed firefighter from further injury–and deteriorating fireground conditions–by operating a hose line from above. While this would not be a normal tactic – under these extreme conditions it may be a necessity.

Rescue Techniques

There are a couple of techniques that can be used to rescue a firefighter who has fallen to a lower level. The technique used will depend on the fire conditions, the structural conditions, any access problems, and the condition of the firefighter. One thing's for sure, it will be a tough rescue no matter which technique is used.

A rescue from below may be performed in one of the following ways:

■ Access and rescue from the floor below

■ Access and rescue from the floor above

Access and Rescue from the Floor Below

It may be possible to gain access to the firefighter from the floor below (the actual level the firefighter has fallen into). If this is possible then the firefighter should be removed from this level.

While there may be obstacles to overcome — moving the firefighter through a breached access point or up a set of stairs — this method will still be easier than trying a rescue from the floor above. *Access is the key to success here.*

Access and Rescue from the Floor Above

If it is not possible to remove the firefighter from the lower level then a rescue will have to be made from above (usually the area directly above where the firefighter fell). There are a few techniques that can be used to perform this type of rescue but they will all be complicated by the same major obstacle – *lifting the entire weight of the firefighter and his gear* up and through the opening.

One problem that may be encountered is that the size of the opening the firefighter fell through may be too small to get the firefighter back up. If this is the case, the opening may have to be expanded to facilitate the rescue.

The opening can be expanded using hand tools or – if conditions allow – power saws. A problem with hand tools (axe or halligan) is the impact that will be created while attempting to make the hole bigger. Power saws present their own problems. Gasoline powered saws (chain saw or circular saw) may not run due to the smoke conditions in the area of the rescue. Battery operated saws (sawzall, etc.) may be a better choice due to their ability to work under the smoke conditions and their smaller size and manageability.

Operating any power saws under interior fireground conditions is extremely dangerous and should be done only as a last resort while ensuring the safety of the rescue crew and the downed firefighter.

To complicate things even further, the rescue team will probably have to deal with active fireground conditions from below during the entire rescue. The rescue is only partially complete when the firefighter is recovered from the lower level—he must then be removed from the structure.

Techniques to recover a firefighter from a lower level:

■ Hose assisted removal

■ Rope assisted removal (Nance/Columbus Technique)

HOSE ASSISTED REMOVAL

If the firefighter that falls through the floor is part of an advancing hose team – or he is encountered or located by an advancing hose team – it may be possible to quickly raise the firefighter out of the hole using the hose line.

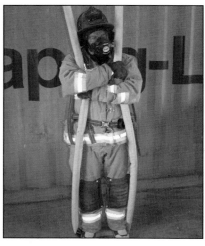

A "U" is formed in the hose line and lowered down into the hole to the firefighter. The firefighter then stands in the "U" and grasps the hose line on both sides. Two or more firefighters then hoist both sides of the line up – at the same rate – and raise the firefighter up to the floor level. When the firefighter is raised up high enough he can attempt to climb out of the hole while getting assistance from above.

If the firefighter is unable to help, or is unconscious, the hose line may still be used but a rescuer will have to be lowered into the opening to assess and package the firefighter and attach him to the hose line. While this method may work, it may be more advantageous to have another RIT follow the hose line in with enough rescue rope to perform a rope assisted removal (see below).

ROPE ASSISTED REMOVAL (NANCE/COLUMBUS TECHNIQUE)

The Nance technique is named for Firefighter John Nance of the Columbus, OH, Fire Department, who died in the line of duty on July 25, 1987, after falling through the floor – into the basement – during a building fire. Multiple attempts were made to rescue Firefighter Nance but none were successful due to a number of factors.

The Nance technique (sometimes referred to as the Columbus technique) involves lowering a rescuer and rope to the downed firefighter. The rope is attached and the firefighter is lifted to the floor above.

Performing the Nance Technique

Again, if the firefighter is conscious the rope can be lowered down to the firefighter where he can attach it to himself and call up to the rescuers to begin the lift.

When the firefighter is unconscious, or unable to assist with the rescue, a rescuer will have to be lowered down (or gain access from below) to assess and package the firefighter, secure an air supply, and apply the rope.

The rope is usually attached directly to the firefighter using the *handcuff knot* (Nance Technique) but it may also be configured as a harness around the firefighter or clipped to a lifting harness or sling on the firefighter.

FIREFIGHTER RESCUE & RAPID INTERVENTION TEAMS

The handcuff knot(s) are normally applied to the wrists/forearm of the firefighter. Although not as common, the knot(s) can also be applied to the ankles for a feet-first lift.

Two knots are definitely better than one when it comes to performing this technique. With only one handcuff knot applied there are only two ends of the rope coming out of the hole that can be used for lifting. Considering the average weight of a firefighter and gear is well over 200 pounds this means that each rescuer will have to *dead lift* at least 100 pounds under fireground conditions. Difficult at best.

With two handcuff knots there are four ends of the rope coming out of the hole. This means that up to four rescuers can be used to perform the lift (often there are only three, the fourth having been lowered to the downed firefighter). Even with three the load is a bit lighter and somewhat easier on the rescuers.

Once the firefighter has been lifted up from the floor below and his body begins to appear through the hole he will have to be lifted onto the floor — *again, easier said than done!* With only three rescuers lifting (which is why it's important to call for additional help early) it

THE HANDCUFF KNOT...

When tying the handcuff knot it's important to remember that there must be enough rope extending on both sides of the knot to reach the floor above. For example, if the downed firefighter is 8–10 feet below then there must be at least 12–14 feet of rope on both sides of the knot so that —when the knot is applied to the firefighter — there is enough rope to reach the firefighters performing the lift.

Firefighters must train and become proficient at estimating the amount of rope needed — and tying the handcuff knot — under realistic fireground conditions.

will be tough to keep the firefighter in the hole while attempting to move/drag him onto the floor. This must be coordinated – and practiced – well before the actual emergency. Many times, the firefighter ends up dropping back into the hole a few feet each time the rescuers try and transition from lifting him vertically to actually moving him out of the hole onto the floor.

The best technique seems to be to have at least two rescuers (more is better) continue to support the weight of the firefighter while one or more grasp the SCBA straps and move him out of the hole onto solid ground.

Once the firefighter has been removed, the rescuer who was lowered to the floor below will have to be raised out of the hole (unless he was able to gain access from below and he can follow that path back to the rest of the team).

Now that the team is back together and the firefighter is out of the hole (also assessed, packaged and air supply secured) he must be removed from the building. (the other part of this rescue).

As we said before — performing this type of rescue is extremely difficult and physically draining on the rescuers. Make sure there is additional help at the rescue location and more on the way in to continue the rescue.

Other Rescue Techniques

The rescue of a firefighter will probably involve multiple techniques to achieve success. In fact, based on prior training and experience, there are likely to be new techniques created in order to overcome the obstacles faced during the rescue.

Remember one thing, failure to prepare and train in the rescue techniques needed will place the entire operation at a disadvantage from the very beginning. *There are no second chances on the fireground!*

PART II
RAPID
INTERVENTION
TEAMS

Rapid Intervention Teams

Training is the key to successful rapid intervention team operations! *There are no second chances on the fireground!* When discussing rapid intervention teams it's important to look at:

■ Why Do We Need Rapid Intervention Teams?

■ The Rapid Intervention Team

■ Rapid Intervention Team Tools and Staging

■ Preparing the Fireground — Proactive RIT Tasks

■ Responding to a MAYDAY — The RIT Deployment

■ Commanding Rapid Intervention Operations

5

Why Do We Need Rapid Intervention Teams?

Because Stuff Happens! The bottom line is that we need rapid intervention teams on the fireground to take care of one of our own who gets into trouble, period!

Translation: for the **SAFETY** of the firefighters who are operating on the fireground.

Before getting into why *others* think we need rapid intervention teams on the fireground let's all agree that trained, competent, rapid intervention teams on the fireground are an absolute necessity for the most important reason of all — firefighter safety.

No matter how much we prepare, no matter how much we train, no matter how good (invincible) we think we are, things go wrong on the fireground and firefighters get into trouble. *That's why <u>we</u> need rapid intervention teams!*

Other Reasons...

Besides firefighter safety, there are a number of reasons that we need rapid intervention teams on the fireground.

- Dynamic fireground
- Inadequate preparation
- The unexpected

DYNAMIC FIREGROUND

The dynamic nature of the fireground continually reinforces the need for rapid intervention teams. *What can go wrong will go wrong — an unfortunate reality.*

Some of the possible fireground situations include: rapid fire spread trapping firefighters; flashover; backdaft; sudden collapse of—or within—the fire building; firefighter(s) disoriented/lost due to changing conditions; loss of water; and more.

INADEQUATE PREPARATION

We cause a lot of our own problems. Many times we don't know what to do, we do it wrong, or we don't have enough people to do it.

Lack of training in the basics of firefighting is a major cause of problems on the fireground. This lack of training leads to fireground emergencies which leads to fire-fighter rescue situations.

Improper tactics is another cause of problems on the fireground that leads to emergency situations. Proper ventilation can eliminate or reduce the chances of back-draft. Choosing the right size line for the amount of fire or type of building can eliminate or reduce the chances of being overrun by fire. The wrong tactics (poor or inad-equate ventilation, the *wrong* size line) tend to get us in trouble.

Not having (or calling) enough people to get the job done also leads to problems on the fireground. Inadequate staffing is an issue faced by most depart-ments but it's no excuse when something goes wrong.

THE UNEXPECTED

Sometimes, no matter how prepared you are, things still go wrong. What you've done to prepare for these times will determine your potential for success. *Murphy* shows up at every incident—sometimes he gets involved and sometimes he doesn't. Prepare for the worst, expect the unexpected.

WHAT DO WE CALL IT...RIT, RIC, FAST?

As stated earlier, the concept of rapid intervention on the fireground involves rescuing one of our own. *The name of the team doesn't make any bit of differ-ence!* Rapid Intervention Team (RIT), Rapid Intervention Crew (RIC), Firefighter Assist and Search Team (FAST), or whatever else you call it in your area simply refers to the team of firefighters who are on the fireground ready to rescue a firefighter (or firefighters) in trouble.

The most important issue regarding the team is their competency—not their name. For consistency sake it would be nice to use the same term across the country but that issue is left for others.

STANDARDS AND REGULATIONS (THE WATCHDOGS)

Standards and regulations are a double-edged sword—they can be used to our advantage and used against us. Basically, we can use them to leverage support but we can also be held accountable if we choose to ignore them.

One advantage of standards and regulations is that they provide *something* that can be referenced and used as a building block for future development. One disadvantage of standards and regulations is that they are never clear cut and are always left up to interpretation (this leads to *selective compliance*).

The end result is that we all see things differently and are able to apply standards and regulations based on our own individual and/or department perceptions. Questions regarding standards and regulations almost always lead to revisions (of the standards or regulations) but seldom lead to clear-cut answers!

Firefighter rescue has been a part of overall fireground operations for a long time — *before any formal standards were put in place to address it.* The formal introduction of rapid intervention teams (in standards) began with the introduction of NFPA 1500, followed by NFPA 1561. Next, the idea of firefighters outside the hazard zone — *prepared to rescue firefighters inside the hazard zone* — was addressed in OSHA 29 CFR 1910.134. Finally, NFPA 1710 and 1720 addressed both an initial and an ongoing rapid intervention team presence on the fireground. As a result of these standards and regulations — *but more importantly for the safety of firefighters operating on the fireground* — rapid intervention capabilities must be provided (and evaluated) on the fireground.

The following standards and regulations reference rapid intervention capabilities in some form:

- **NFPA 1500** — Standard on Fire Department Occupational Safety and Health Program

- **NFPA 1561** — Standard on Emergency Services Incident Management System

- **NFPA 1710** — Standard on Organization and Deployment of Fire Suppression Operations, Emergency Medical Operations, and Special Operations to the Public by Career Fire Departments

- **NFPA 1720** — Standard on Organization and Deployment of Fire Suppression Operations, Emergency Medical Operations, and Special Operations to the Public by Volunteer Fire Departments

- **NFPA 1981** — Standard on Open-Circuit Self-Contained Breathing Apparatus for Fire and Emergency Services

- **OSHA 29 CFR 1910.134** — Occupational Safety and Health Standards – Personal Protective Equipment – Respiratory Protection

The double-edged sword here is that the references exist but do little to help with the practical application and actual implementation of the RIT concept on the fireground.

The interpretation of the above standards and regulations could fill volumes and is not our focus. It is recommended that all firefighters and departments acquire and read the information in these (and other) standards and regulations as additional reference on the subject of rapid intervention.

However, none of the above listed standards and regulations will eliminate the need for the actual training required to perform rapid intervention operations. In fact, after participating in realistic firefighter survival, firefighter rescue, and rapid intervention team training a new appreciation of the advantages and disadvantages of these standards and regulations may be developed.

THE REALITY OF RAPID INTERVENTION OPERATIONS...

The term *Rapid Intervention* is a bit misleading. Performing a firefighter rescue on the fireground is anything but *rapid*. In fact, it's a time-consuming, labor-intensive, process.

A rapid intervention operation on the fireground is an *incident within an incident* that will take solid leadership (Command), multiple rapid intervention teams, and time.

6

The Rapid Intervention Team

The rapid intervention team (RIT) is the crew — or more than likely in the event of an actual emergency, crews — that is assembled on the fireground to prepare for and perform firefighter rescue.

The RIT, as with any other operating crew on the fireground (engine company, truck company), must know their job and be given the proper tools, leadership, latitude, and training to perform it.

DEVELOP A RAPID INTERVENTION TEAM STANDARD OPERATING PROCEDURE (SOP)

Some departments write SOPs for everything (everything!), others don't even have them. Fireground SOPs serve multiple purposes — if you let them. First, they give some sense of direction when arriving on the scene and beginning initial operations. Sure, nine-times-out-of-ten the fireground companies don't even think about the SOPs—but that's because they know them and have been trained to perform that way so their actions are instinctive. But, every now and then the SOPs are referred to during initial operations—and it's at these times that they make all the difference in the world.

The second purpose is that SOPs provide department-specific review material. They're a great way to review the basic fireground operations that should take place — first engine, first truck, second engine, second truck, etc. when responding.

RIT operations are no different. In fact, because of the intense nature of a fireground RIT operation, having an SOP is even more critical. Outline how the department will deal with RIT on the fireground. Identify the team and positions, the tools and need for staging, the proactive tasks that may be needed. **Develop a functional RIT SOP — *one that's designed and written to HELP during a RIT operation.***

One of the biggest reasons SOPs fail is because they try and remove the most important department resource from the fireground — a firefighter's common sense and ability to THINK! With RIT operations, the RIT has to think and interpret what's going on — and act based on the information. Give them an SOP that allows them to operate — and, hopefully, succeed!

FIREGROUND FUNCTIONS OF THE RAPID INTERVENTION TEAM

Before discussing team positions and assignments it's important to identify the fireground functions of the RIT, they include:

- Arrive prepared and capable of performing the functions of the RIT.

- Communicate with Command/Rescue Sector.

- Stage and secure appropriate tools and equipment.

- Continually assess RIT resource needs (tools and teams).

- Continually size-up the fireground — fire conditions and structure.

- Continually monitor the crews operating on the fireground — location and condition.

- Continually prepare the fireground (proactive tasks) to prevent firefighter emergencies.

- Provide immediate deployment in the event of a firefighter emergency (MAYDAY).

- Search for, locate, assess, package and rescue those firefighters who require it.

- Do not become part of the rescue problem.

WHO SHOULD MAKE UP THE RAPID INTERVENTION TEAM?

The type of company that should make up the RIT is an area that stimulates a lot of discussion. Should it be a Truck Company? Should it be an Engine Company?

Should it be a Rescue Company? Should it be a hybrid of companies made up on the fireground?

There is no right or wrong answer to this question. The reality of RIT operations on the fireground is that somebody (a trained company) must be there to do the job. Every fireground (and department) is staffed differently. There are advantages and disadvantages to each type of company being used as the RIT on the fireground. There will be times that all of these companies will have to be used.

Train all companies to perform RIT operations and then use those companies that are available at the time. When it comes to the minimum tools needed to perform RIT (see the chapter on RIT Tools and Staging) make sure that they're available on every fireground (having them on every apparatus would be ideal).

Depending on the type and difficulty of the RIT operation, specialty teams (equipment and training) may be required to get the job done. While it would be great if all members of the department were trained in all of the specialty areas that may be required (rope rescue, building collapse and shoring, etc.), it's not realistic. The reality is that once the victim has been located, the RIT may be moved into a support role that assists the specialty team. Prepare for these situations ahead of time and make provisions to get these special teams to the fireground as soon as possible.

So, whether it's an Engine Company, Truck Company or Rescue Company make sure that the members are proficient at performing RIT operations. Training just one company in the department to perform as a RIT is not a good idea. *What happens if that company is the one that gets in trouble and requires assistance?*

RAPID INTERVENTION TEAM STAFFING

When talking about rapid intervention team staffing on the fireground it's important to look at:

■ Individual RIT staffing

■ Number of RITs needed

How Many Firefighters Should Make Up the Rapid Intervention Team?

The answer to this question often identifies the differ-ence between theory and reality. Some think that two mem-bers can get the job done but nothing could be further from the truth. **A mini-mum of four (4) firefighters should make up the RIT.** In

the ideal setting, where staffing is not an issue, the ideal RIT size is four (4) members—*Officer, Navigation/Air Supply, 2 Search Firefighters.* In addition, there would be multiple RITs available on the fireground which would allow one team to be in stand-by mode, ready to deploy to a MAYDAY, while additional teams could perform proactive tasks. Where staffing is not ideal (which is in most departments) then there should be *no less* than 3 members assigned to the RIT—*Officer, Navigation/Air Supply, 1 Search Firefighter.* **The bottom line is that you must have a capable team ready to deploy immediately—*or you really don't have a RIT in place.***

How Many Rapid Intervention Teams Will Be Needed?

The size and/or complexity of the fireground will determine the number of RITs that are needed at the outset. While one RIT may initially be deployed for residences, multiple RITs may be required for large commercial structures and high-rise buildings.

A RIT component (made up of multiple teams from the outset) would be the ideal solution — but we all know what it takes for that to happen!

During actual rapid intervention operations on the fireground multiple RITs will be needed. Any time a RIT is deployed additional RITs must be put in place for their relief and safety.

The reality of rapid intervention operations is that it will probably take two or more teams to actually remove a downed firefighter. Sure, if everything falls into place the first RIT may locate, package and remove the downed firefighter. More than likely, however, the first team will probably be used to locate the firefighter and secure his air supply while additional teams will be used to actually extricate and remove him.

RAPID INTERVENTION TEAM ASSIGNMENTS

There are many individual tasks that members of the RIT must perform. These tasks can be broken down into *proactive tasks before a MAYDAY* and *tasks performed when responding to a MAYDAY*. While it would be great to assign all of these tasks ahead of time, it is not realistic.

Some of the proactive tasks on the fireground are found on every incident (size-up, 360° survey of structure, tool staging, etc.) but many are dependent on the fireground and structure (laddering, forcible entry/egress challenges, etc.). It would be impossible to pre-assign all of these tasks. What is realistic, is to train all members on how to perform each of the tasks and then assign them based on the incident.

Remember this: If you don't have a RIT that is immediately ready to deploy to a MAYDAY then you don't have a RIT, you have a team doing support functions!

The tasks performed when responding to a MAYDAY (once the RIT is activated on the fireground) are much more specific. These tasks can, and should, be assigned at the start of the shift. RIT members should be proficient at performing all of these tasks, as well.

RAPID INTERVENTION TEAM POSITIONS

Pre-assigned positions and assignments are critical to the success of any fireground team and the RIT is no exception. While it really doesn't matter what you call the actual positions—*competency is what's really important*—a name that reflects the basic function helps make things easier to remember. The positions that must be in place when a RIT deploys to a MAYDAY are:

- The RIT Officer
- Navigation/Air Supply
- Search

Once the victim has been located the Navigation/Air Supply and Search firefighters assume the role of *Packaging and Removal*, under the direction of the RIT Officer. (It may take two or more RITs to complete the entire removal.)

The RIT Officer

The most important position on the RIT is the RIT Officer. RIT leadership prior to and during an actual fireground emergency is crucial to overall success. The RIT Officer should take a proactive role regarding RIT operations at the start of the shift by making individual assignments in the event the company is dispatched as the RIT.

Once on the fireground it's very important for the RIT Officer to have a strong presence. Discipline is a must during all fireground operations—especially RIT operations—and the RIT Officer must practice it and demand it from the members of the team.

When preparing the fireground and performing proactive tasks the RIT Officer must ensure that the team is ready to deploy immediately, that RIT members are performing all of the needed tasks, and that Command is kept informed of the current status and what's going on. Knowledge of current fireground conditions and anticipation of future fireground conditions (initial and ongoing size-up of the fire, the building and the companies) is an essential part of the RIT Officer's duties.

In the event that the RIT is deployed to locate and assist a firefighter, the RIT Officer must coordinate and direct the interior actions of the RIT. Prior to entry the RIT Officer must ensure that the needed equipment is assembled, that a RIT tag line is secured outside the structure, that all members are clear on their assignments, and that the RIT has a plan.

Having a plan and making sure that all team members understand it is one of the most important things the RIT Officer must do when entering to rescue a firefighter. It's too late to put a plan together once the MAYDAY is declared and the team has been deployed!

The RIT Officer should have a thermal imaging camera (if available) to assist with navigation, movement, and possible location of the firefighter(s). The thermal camera should be used as another tool to aid in the RIT operation. The camera should increase speed and efficiency during the operation but it should never be relied on 100%. You will still need to use all of your fireground senses to search for and locate the firefighter as well as keep track of your way out of the structure.

In addition, he must also ensure that the Navigation/Air Supply Firefighter (see below) has secured the tag line to the outside and is ready to deploy it during the operation. The tag line is critical for two reasons. First, the tag line provides a direct exit out of the structure for the RIT. Equally important, the tag line provides a direct avenue (if it's managed correctly) to the RIT/victim for additional RITs. Since it's unlikely that one team will be able to accomplish the entire process of location and removal of the firefighter the tag line plays a vital role in the success of the overall operation.

The RIT Officer must coordinate and direct the actual search effort for the missing firefighter(s). The search is conducted by the RIT members assigned the Search position. Ideally there will be two Search firefighters that are performing the actual search. These firefighters should be directed by the RIT Officer based on information gathered from the thermal camera, the surroundings, any radio reports, and prior fireground experience.

When the victim is found the RIT Officer MUST take control of the tag line from the Navigation/Air Supply firefighter and securely tie the tag line off somewhere near the victims' location (but NEVER to the actual victim). At this point the RIT Officer maintains contact with the tag line and guides the other members out during the removal process.

The RIT Officer is also responsible for communicating information to Command or the Rescue Sector during the deployment. Where is the RIT? What are the conditions? What problems are being encountered? What additional resources are needed? What is the air supply status of the team? All of this information, and more, must be communicated while the interior operation is being conducted.

The RIT Officer should be the most experienced member of the team. There are many critical tasks that must be performed, simultaneously, in order for things to succeed — missing any one of the tasks may cause the mission to fail.

Navigation/Air Supply

The second RIT position involves navigation and air supply. The Navigation/Air Supply firefighter deploys the tag line after securing it to the outside prior to entry. During the operation this team member deploys and manages the tag line (to keep the shortest, straightest, route from the outside to the RIT).

In addition, this member brings in the emergency air supply (additional SCBA or RIT Pack) and is responsible for securing the air supply of the downed firefighter when located *(with the help of one of the search fire-*

fighters). As discussed earlier, securing the air may be as simple as swapping a regulator or as complicated as removing and replacing the entire SCBA face piece. Depending on the difficulty, additional help may be needed.

Finding a comfortable and secure means of transporting the emergency air supply, while deploying and managing the RIT tag line, is something that should be practiced and prepared for ahead of time. While it's not a complicated set of tasks each one is vital to the success of the RIT operation. *The search firefighters would be slowed if they had to transport the air supply while conducting searches.*

Once the firefighter is located the RIT Officer takes control of the tag line from the Navigation/Air Supply firefighter so the Navigation/Air Supply firefighter can move up and secure the air supply to the downed firefighter.

In the event that the first RIT is unable to locate the firefighter the RIT Officer and the Navigation/Air Supply firefighter should work together to make sure the tag line is secured at the current location prior to exiting. Ideally, a second or additional RIT will be arriving prior to the first team leaving (this requires proactive actions on the part of the RIT Officer and Command or the Rescue Sector).

While the use of the emergency air supply is intended for the downed firefighter, the reality is that it may also be used by the RIT. In the event that RIT members run low on air or get into trouble the emergency air supply may have to be used to assist them in exiting the building. For this reason, each incoming RIT should bring their own emergency air supply. If it's not used during the rescue it should be brought out for the same reason.

Search Firefighters (2)

Along with the RIT Officer and the Navigation/ Air Supply firefighter, the RIT should have members assigned to the actual Search function. **Remember, before the RIT can do anything else to help the downed firefighter they must find him!** All too often the RIT members are so overloaded with tools and assignments prior to enter-

ing the building that the actual search effort is all but forgotten. A four person RIT allows two members to be assigned the Search function. **The main function of the Search firefighters is to SEARCH!** The Search firefighters follow the direction of the RIT Officer and aggressively search for the missing firefighter(s). As we discussed in Chapter 2, *Searching for a Firefighter*, any and all means should be used to search for and find the firefighter.

RIT members should always be in voice contact with each other. Aggressive searching requires maintaining an awareness of your location— that's why voice contact and the RIT tag line play such an important part of the operation.

Remember, a breakdown in discipline at this stage of the operation will only prolong the search and potentially cause the mission to fail. When searching for a firefighter it is important to follow the RIT Officer's lead (another reason that a strong presence by the RIT Officer is critical).

Packaging and Removal

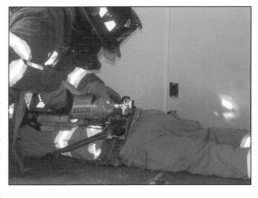

Once the firefighter(s) has been located a number of tasks must be performed simultaneously. While these tasks should be assigned at the start of the shift it is wise for the RIT Officer to make sure all tasks are accounted for by confirming the assignments once the firefighter(s) has been located.

RIT OFFICER

The RIT Officer must notify Command or the Rescue Sector that the firefighter(s) has been located and that assessment and packaging are underway (benchmark). He must also take control of the tag line from the Navigation/Air Supply firefighter and secure it somewhere near the victims' location. The RIT Officer must maintain contact with the tag line for the duration of the interior operation.

The RIT Officer should also confirm that the RIT members are performing their packaging and removal assignments. In addition to these things, he must quickly evaluate and give an update on the interior conditions of the fire, the building, the downed firefighter(s), and the RIT members (including air supply). An additional RIT should also be requested to assist with the rescue—if it hasn't already been requested or deployed automatically per the SOP. Finally, the RIT Officer needs to review and communicate the rescue/removal plan (and have a backup plan — or two — ready to go) to all RIT members and Command or the Rescue Sector.

SEARCH FIREFIGHTER (WHO FOUND THE VICTIM)

This firefighter must immediately let all members know that he has found the victim. Before getting involved with any other tasks the firefighter must confirm that the other team members are moving to his location. The next step is to reset the victims PASS device and check the immediate condition of the victim (breathing, entanglement, etc.).

At this point the Search firefighter should convert the victim's SCBA waist strap to an improvised drag harness by loosening the waist strap, disconnecting it, and reconnecting it between the legs (crotch) of the downed firefighter. This action will provide a great benefit during the removal process. It helps keep the SCBA on the downed firefighter and it helps secure the SCBA so it can be used to drag the victim.

SECOND SEARCH FIREFIGHTER (IF PRESENT)

After converging on the victim's location, the second Search firefighter performs a quick sweep around the immediate area looking for an alternate exit location (door or window). Many times this simple sweep can prevent the time-consuming removal of following the tag line all the way back out of the building. If an exit is found, he moves back to the RIT

Officer and extends the tag line from the tie off location to the new exit location and secures it there. This helps provide a direct route to the exit for additional RITs and for the removal operation.

NAVIGATION/AIR SUPPLY FIREFIGHTER

Once the tag line is passed off to the RIT Officer the Navigation/Air Supply firefighter moves up to the victim location and secures the air supply and attaches the RIT air pack to the victim.

It's very important to note that the above packaging and removal steps are all occurring simultaneously. Also, they are occurring rapidly. There isn't a lot of time to stop and think — this is where prior training really pays off.

When it comes to the actual removal operation the RIT Officer must maintain control and order as the rescue proceeds. This portion of the rescue effort will be intense and physically exhausting. The RIT Officer should rotate members of the RIT through the various rescue positions so they don't become exhausted and unable to continue.

There may be additional tasks that must be performed as part of the interior RIT operation but the above tasks represent those that should be an integral part of all RIT training and preparation.

ESSENTIAL TOOLS (ALL MEMBERS)

RIT tools and staging will be discussed in the next chapter. What's important to mention here is that when the first RIT is deployed to locate, secure, package, and remove a downed firefighter that a basic compliment of tools be carried by each member.

Radio

All RIT members should have and use a radio. All members should carry a portable radio and make sure that it is on the correct fireground channel. The battery should be checked at the start of the shift and changed after major incidents. The radio should be equipped with a lapel microphone. The fact is that it's tough to hear on the fireground even under ideal conditions. When radios are carried in pockets the speaker is (at a minimum) down on your chest away from your ear. With a lapel microphone the speaker is moved up closer to your ear giving you a better chance of hearing radio traffic.

Flashlight

All RIT members should carry flashlights. Personal flashlights are great but should be secondary to larger hand-lanterns during RIT operations. Larger hand lanterns are more appropriate for RIT operations due to their brighter and stronger beams.

Hand Tools

All RIT members should carry hand tools. While some would argue that not every member needs a hand tool the argument is usually about personal preference on the fireground, not what a RIT member should or should not carry. Whether your preference is carrying a tool or not, during RIT operations it's wise for all members to carry some type of hand tool (at least one set of *irons* should be made up among the RIT members).

A little bit of training, moving around under realistic conditions while using/carrying a hand tool (in addition to the other equipment that you'll need to carry as part of the RIT) is all it takes to become proficient at carrying a tool during these operations.

Survival Gear

In addition, all personal protective equipment should be worn and personal survival gear should be carried (all the time, not just during RIT operations). Personal survival gear includes:

- Wire cutters
- Knife
- Door chocks
- Personal rope (20-40 feet)
- Webbing

There may be additional gear that you carry but these basic tools should always be a part of your personal survival gear.

7

Rapid Intervention Team Tools and Staging

The tools used to perform rapid intervention operations on the fireground, and where these tools should be staged, is an area that receives a considerable amount of debate. The type and amount of tools needed by the RIT will be largely determined by the type of structure they are operating in and type of problem they are trying to solve.

Every RIT should have a basic set of tools — *no matter what type of building or problem.* Additional tools, beyond the basic set, will be dictated by the specific incident. Part of the ongoing size-up of the RIT is to identify hazards and concerns that may increase the difficulty of getting the job done. Identifying and requesting additional tools that may be needed to deal with these hazards and concerns should begin as soon as possible.

RAPID INTERVENTION TEAM STAGING AREA

A RIT staging area should be set up on every incident. Depending on the size of the structure (and/or incident), multiple RIT staging areas may be needed. The RIT staging area will, at most incidents, also serve as the RIT tools staging area. In fact, this is probably the best set-up because it allows the team to have its tools in one location — ready to go — when/if they are deployed to assist a distressed firefighter.

RIT Staging Location

Where should the RIT be staged? This is another area that is constantly being discussed.

The bottom line is that the RIT (and the tools that will be needed initially) should be staged as close as possible to the entrance that will—most likely—be used to begin the search for the firefighter in trouble.

Many departments *(Incident Commanders)* feel that the RIT should be right beside the Command Post, not doing anything but waiting to be deployed. This is more of a control thing than a proactive fireground safety measure. The problem with this *control theory* is that the Command Post shouldn't be anywhere near the most likely RIT entrance—it should be a little further back allowing a broader view of the structure (incident). The reality of the RIT operation is that some of the RIT members will be performing proactive RIT functions around the fireground while the  remainder of the team will be standing by (near the most-likely entrance) to immediately begin the search—*if deployed!* Communication with Command—which is part of the initial and ongoing functions of the RIT—can be accomplished using a combination of face-to-face (when possible) and radio communications during the incident.

Depending on the size of the structure there may be a need for multiple RIT staging areas, and actual teams. One of the biggest factors affecting this decision is the amount of actual equipment available. Most departments don't have the luxury of equipping multiple RIT tool staging areas — let alone multiple teams — at the beginning of an incident so a location closest to a known entry point may be the best solution. If one RIT tool staging area is set up and there are multiple RITs positioned on the fireground then the location of the RIT tool staging area should be announced to all teams. At a minimum, the RIT tools required to deploy immediately should be kept with each team.

RAPID INTERVENTION TEAM TOOLS

This is where things tend to get out of control when talking about RIT operations on the fireground. A simple RIT operation may only require a pair of wire cutters to disentangle a firefighter. On the other extreme, a complex RIT operation may require a complete collapse rescue unit (with all of the associated lifting and shoring equipment) to extricate a company of firefighters trapped beneath a collapse within the structure.

Successful RIT tool staging should strive for a happy medium at the outset. The tools kept in the staging area should be continually assessed and adjusted based on the ongoing size-up of both the fireground situation and the RIT operation. As the saying goes: *you can always send the equipment home if it's not needed — but you can never get it there quick enough when it's already needed.*

Setting up the RIT tool staging area and collecting all the tools required should be an assignment (made at the beginning of the shift) that should begin immediately after the staging location has been determined. In fact, many of the tools to be placed in the staging area should be brought to the scene as the RIT approaches.

There is no one complete list of RIT tools that may be needed. The best possible description/list of tools is probably stated in the following terms — *RIT operations may require all of the tools that you've ever used on the fireground, and then some.*

Proficiency With RIT Tools

Before discussing the different types of tools that may be needed for RIT operations one important point must be stressed. **RIT members must be proficient with the operation of the tools that may be used during RIT operations.**

Searching for a firefighter who is trapped and running out of air is not the time to try and learn how to use a thermal imaging camera! The same holds true for all of the tools used for RIT operations.

Frequent training on RIT tools should be conducted. During these training sessions members can refresh where the tools are carried on the different apparatus and — *more importantly* — how the tools operate.

Essential RIT Tools Carried By Every Member of the Team

The essential tools that should be carried by each member of the RIT were discussed at the end of the last chapter. **These tools are repeated here to stress their importance.**

- Radio with Lapel Microphone

- Flashlight

- Hand Tools

- Survival Gear

Basic RIT Tools

In addition to the essential set of tools that every RIT member should carry, there are basic tools that every RIT should have on the fireground. Some of these tools will be used before the RIT deployment (to prepare the fireground) some will be used during the interior RIT operation (to search for, package, and remove the firefighter) and some will be used to rescue/remove the firefighter. If these tools are not carried on all department apparatus they must be made available on the fireground if RIT operations are to be successful.

At a minimum, the tools staged with the RIT at the staging area should include:

■ RIT air pack(s)

■ RIT tag line

■ Irons

■ Pike poles

■ Ground ladder(s) for upper floor access *(deployed – not staged)*

■ Rescue rope

■ EMS equipment (Oxygen, Defibrillator)

■ Thermal imaging camera (sleep mode in staging)

■ RIT tactical worksheet/checklist

■ Lighting source for staging area (additional hand lanterns work for this)

The following sections discuss additional equipment that may/will be used and should be staged by the RIT. If equipment is used for proactive tasks (saws, etc.) then it should be placed back into the staging area when the tasks have been completed.

RIT Tools Used Before the MAYDAY

Part of the overall RIT operation on the fireground involves preparing the fireground in an attempt to prevent an actual emergency from occurring—*or to make it easier to deal with an emergency if one happens.* Tools that may be used during this *proactive* phase of the RIT operations on the fireground include:

■ Ground ladders (for access and egress)

■ Hand tools (for forcible entry/egress)

■ Power saws (for forcible entry/egress)

■ Secure water supply (for potential hose line use)

■ Aerial apparatus (proactive placement)

- RIT Tactical Worksheet (for monitoring)
- Radios for monitoring fireground traffic (if different frequencies/channels are used)
- Additional or specialty tools...
- Additional RITs

Other tools may be required and used, depending on the type of structure or the fireground conditions. Fires at commercial occupancies may require different tools than those at residential occupancies (ie. metal cutting versus wood cutting blades, etc.).

RIT Tools Used During the Search

When a fireground MAYDAY is declared — or any other time that the RIT is deployed to search for a missing or distressed firefighter — the team (or a portion of it) must be ready to deploy, immediately.

When the RIT deploys there is a basic set of equipment that should be brought in with them. In addition to the essential RIT member tools, the following equipment should be brought in:

- Tag line
- Thermal camera
- RIT air pack
- Hand tools
- Rescue rope
- Webbing/Sling-Link
- Search rope system (for large areas) if needed
- Additional RITs (if needed)

During this phase of the operation, finding the firefighter(s) is the most important task. The interior team must be able to move through the structure quickly without being weighed down by a lot of equipment.

By deploying and managing a tag line additional equipment that is needed for the rescue (see below) can be brought directly to the RIT after the firefighter has been located.

RIT Tools Used During the Rescue

Once the firefighter has been located and the initial assessment of the firefighter and the situation has been completed, additional tools that may be required to rescue the firefighter can be called for and brought in.

It would be nice to list all of the tools that may be needed during the rescue of a firefighter, but it's not possible. The amount and type of equipment that's needed is completely dependent on the situation found — *which is why the assessment is critical.* Additional tools and equipment that may be needed includes:

■ Additional RITs

■ Specialty rescue teams (collapse, etc.)

■ Hose line for protection

■ Air bags for lifting debris

■ Extrication equipment

  Cutters

  Spreaders

  Battery or hydraulic (depends on location)

■ Cribbing

- Stokes/backboard
- Power saws (battery, gas)
- Additional RIT air packs (air supply)
- Additional ground ladders
- Simple mechanical advantage systems

  Lifting/lowering

  Dragging
- *Whatever else it takes...*

Additional RIT Tools...Whatever It Takes!

A complete list of tools is just not possible. The above lists represent a lot of the equipment that may be needed for a successful RIT operation.

The reality is that the tools carried on the department apparatus are the tools that will be immediately available for use. Preplanning and prior training will help determine what additional tools may be needed. If you can't acquire them ahead of time then determine where you'll be able to get them during an emergency. Remember, if you're calling for them during an emergency it may already be too late.

As stated earlier, *RIT operations may require all of the tools that you've ever used on the fireground, and then some.* Don't wait until a fireground MAYDAY is underway to determine that you don't have the needed equipment—or department members lack the proper training and proficiency—to get the job done. Preplan and train — firefighters' lives depend on it!

8

Preparing the Fireground: Proactive RIT Tasks

Another area of RIT operations that generates differing opinions is what a RIT should be allowed to do on the fireground before an actual emergency is declared.

Some Incident Commanders believe that the RIT should be *glued* to the Command Post awaiting a fireground MAYDAY. On the other hand, other Incident Commanders believe that the RIT should be used just like any other fireground company (put to use where needed) until the incident is brought under control.

RIT operations on the fireground should fall somewhere in between these two extremes. Under ideal circumstances there would be a *rapid intervention sector* on the fireground that is staffed by multiple companies. Some of the companies would be performing proactive tasks while others would be standing by ready to deploy if needed. Unfortunately, we don't work under ideal conditions so we must develop a way to perform proactive RIT tasks while keeping a team ready to go. Remember, *if you can prevent an emergency situation from developing then you limit the chances of having to perform a rescue.*

Proactive RIT tasks on the fireground actually begin during the response (initial size-up) and continue until the RIT is released from the scene. If the RIT is actually deployed to a MAYDAY then their mode switches from performing proactive tasks to rescue.

PROACTIVE RIT TASKS ON THE FIREGROUND INCLUDE:

- Proactive RIT dispatch

- Performing a RIT size-up

- Setting up a RIT staging area(s)

- Ensuring fireground accountability

- Monitoring the fireground, the structure, and the companies

- Preparing the fireground

  Providing secondary egress/access locations

  Removing any hazards and/or obstacles

Performing any other tasks that may prevent an emergency from occurring

■ Ensuring adequate RIT resources to be ready to deploy, immediately, to search for and rescue a firefighter

These proactive tasks are continuous and ongoing. No one task can exclude another—they are all equally important. As you can see, the size of the RIT becomes extremely important when considering this *proactive* approach to RIT operations. Monitoring the fireground, ensuring adequate access and egress, *and* maintaining a ready search team all requires preplanning and prior training if the tasks are to be accomplished on the fireground.

PROACTIVE RIT DISPATCH

The RIT should be dispatched with the initial companies. Too many departments wait until a fire has been confirmed before dispatching a RIT. By this time the fireground operation is well underway. Fireground operations are front-loaded and time sensitive! The information during the initial arrival and set-up of the first-due companies may be critical to the RIT mission.

As with all fireground operations — playing catch-up is something that doesn't work! By handicapping the RIT from the outset the entire operation may be compromised. If the fire is brought under control quickly, and the RIT is not needed, then the RIT can be disregarded.

Consider changing your department dispatch protocol so that a RIT is started as part of the initial alarm— *anticipate problems and prepare ahead of time instead of simply reacting to them when they occur.*

PERFORMING A RIT SIZE-UP

The RIT size-up is something that should begin as soon as the alarm is received. The actual size-up can be broken down into the following areas:

Dispatch/Response

Once the dispatch is received, and during the response, the RIT should begin their size-up of the incident. What is the address? What type of structure is it? What companies are responding? What is the reported problem? Is it a confirmed fire? Have you been there before? The list goes on.

Once the actual fireground size-up is given over the radio (from the first-arriving company) the RIT should factor this *more reliable* information into their initial plan. Who gave the report? How did they sound? Is this a confirmed incident? Did you learn anything new from this *actual* fireground size-up?

Fireground Size-up

As with any responding company, the RIT should perform a fireground size-up when it arrives on scene. What is visible? How does the *picture* differ from the previous information gathered? Is the condition better or worse than expected? Are there any immediate hazards that stand out? What's the smoke condition telling you? What's the fire condition telling you?

Building Size-up

What type of building is it and how is that going to help, or hurt, RIT operations? What type of problems will the building create for the operating crews? How will these problems affect the RIT's ability to get them out if they get into trouble? Is the building strong or weak? Is the fire condition rapidly deteriorating the building's condition? Is this a *winner* or a *loser*?

360° Survey of the Fireground

Performing a 360° survey of the fireground (and building) is an essential part of the RIT operation. This survey should be done as soon as possible after the RIT

arrives, *and it should be repeated frequently during the incident.* The information gathered during the 360° survey should be shared with all members of the RIT!

The 360° survey is an attempt, by the RIT, to *define* the playing field. What current problems exist and must be corrected? What problems should be anticipated? Are there additional access/egress points that can be used? Are there access/egress problems that must be addressed (forcible entry, chained doors, barred windows…)? Are fire conditions different — better or worse — around the structure?

The information gathered during the 360° survey, along with the other size-up information that's been obtained, is used to formulate a plan to *proactively* prepare the fireground — trying to prevent an emergency.

The Big Picture

Don't get tunnel vision — and don't take the RIT size-up lightly! The function of the RIT is to try and prevent a fireground emergency—if possible—and to successfully deal with one if it happens. Information gathering and processing (initial and ongoing size-up) is an essential task that the RIT must perform.

Size-up is cumulative! Factoring all of the information gathered — throughout the incident — gives a more complete picture of what's going on. Discarding information that *didn't seem important at the time* often leads to increased problems on the fireground.

SETTING UP A RIT STAGING AREA

Setting up a RIT staging area is a given. Determining the location of the staging area is something that must be done as soon as possible after the RIT arrives on scene. As RIT members approach the scene they should bring as many of the basic RIT tools as possible with them. Once the staging location has been determined they can assemble the tools there.

One proactive assignment that should be made at the start of the shift is who will set up the RIT staging area. While many of the tools can be brought to the scene by the RIT members, additional tools may have to be gathered after arrival. Gathering these tools, while keeping a RIT ready to deploy, is just one of the many juggling acts that will have to be performed as part of the RIT operation.

ENSURING FIREGROUND ACCOUNTABILITY

One of the proactive functions of the RIT, like it or not, is maintaining or tracking accountability on the fireground. Tracking accountability begins as soon as the RIT becomes a part of the incident. During the response the RIT should monitor radio traffic to identify the companies operating on the fireground. The RIT's role in accountability addresses:

- Who's operating on the fireground
- Where companies are operating
- Working within the ICS

Who's operating on the fireground

As the RIT develops a game plan for operations it must constantly identify who is operating on the fireground. Who were the initial companies? Are they still in the structure or have they come out? Are there extra

companies on the fireground? Any mutual aid companies? Are they operating on the same radio frequency? Do they wear the same type SCBA?

Where companies are operating

This information is critical! Is the fireground divided into Sectors? Are there companies operating on multiple floor levels? Are companies updating Command of their position? Keeping track of where companies are operating on the fireground allows the RIT to deploy to a *probable* location if something goes wrong. Tracking company locations should, hopefully, narrow down the initial search area (a big part of the *rapid*) if something happens!

Working within the ICS

The RIT must also be held accountable. When arriving on scene the RIT should enter the ICS by reporting to Command. Depending on the department ICS structure—as it relates to RIT operations—the RIT may report to (or become) the Rescue Sector, or it may simply report to Command *(see Commanding Rapid Intervention Operations)*. Once in the system, the RIT should operate and perform its fireground functions within the system.

The RIT should also communicate with the Safety Officer. Maintaining an open line of communication with both the Safety Officer and the Incident Commander will help keep needed information flowing on the fireground.

MONITORING THE FIREGROUND

Monitoring the fireground begins with the initial size-up and continues throughout the entire RIT operation. The best way to monitor the fireground — and keep track of the information — is to use a RIT Tactical Worksheet/Checklist. Like any tactical worksheet, the RIT Tactical Worksheet is simply a form/checklist that is used to help RIT members *recall* and *record* important RIT information. The worksheet doesn't need to be fancy but is should address the following information:

- Building construction type and inherent problems (including building dimensions, number of floors, whether or not there's a basement, type of roof construction, etc.)

- Crews operating on scene

- Crew locations and assignments

- Condition of crews as they exit the structure

- Fireground conditions (getting better or worse)
- Structural conditions (getting better or worse)
- Fireground times (overall time, operating times...)
- Fireground radio frequencies
- Known hazards
- Diagram of fireground/structure
- Possible access/egress locations
- Location of Command Post, Medical Station
- Location of RIT staging area(s)
- Additional resources in staging (apparatus, equipment, personnel...)
- Other information relative to RIT operations and the fireground operation

Remember, the worksheet/checklist is only as good as the information that it records. For instance, simply putting down that E-1 is fire attack won't do any good when E-1 declares a MAYDAY! Where is E-1 operating (first floor, second floor, basement...)? How many members are in E-1's crew? How long has E-1 been operating inside?

In addition to maintaining a tactical worksheet, monitoring the fireground involves ANTICIPATING PROBLEMS based on the information being gathered.

Monitoring the fireground means paying attention to all of the details! It is an ACTIVE RIT position that must not be taken lightly. The information gathered should be constantly shared with all members of the RIT so that everyone is on the same page. The RIT should have an initial *plan* and constantly update/revise that *plan* based on new information.

PREPARING THE FIREGROUND

With a RIT tools staging area set up and an initial 360° survey of the fireground accomplished the RIT can begin *preparing* the actual fireground. During this phase of RIT operations, members of the RIT perform tasks that make the fireground safer (preventing a possible emergency) and more accessible (in the event that the RIT is deployed). Remember also that during this phase of the operation there must be members of the RIT standing by and ready to deploy, immediately, if needed.

Providing Secondary Egress/Access

The most common type of secondary egress/access that the RIT can provide is placement of ground ladders to upper floors when members are operating at multi-story structures. Sure, ladders should be placed to all sides of a structure as a part of normal operating duties — but that doesn't always happen.

Members of the RIT should bring one, or more, ladders as they approach the structure. If ladders have already been placed to all sides of the structure then these additional ladders can be staged. If there are additional windows (without ladders) then the ladders can be thrown as an added margin of safety.

Don't forget about the roof. If companies are operating on the roof then make sure they have two means of egress.

Removing Entry/Egress Hazards

A major fireground hazard that must be addressed is the removal of high-security building features. A common security feature that is found on many occupancies (more common at commercial structures) is burglar bars on windows. These bars are designed to keep people out of the structure. However, during firefighting operations they may trap firefighters in the structure. These bars must be removed if crews are operating in the building!

In addition to window bars, there are many other entry/egress hazards that may have to be addressed by the RIT. Chained entrances, roll-down security doors, scissor gates — basically forcible entry challenges —

must all be *opened up* when companies are working inside a structure.

Another serious hazard that exists is covered windows. Many structures — either under renovation or abandoned —

have their windows boarded over with plywood or some other material. These coverings could trap firefighters inside during interior operations. These coverings should also be removed to facilitate  potential emergency exits or RIT access.

Additional Proactive Tasks...Whatever!

Every fireground is different. Part of the proactive function of the RIT is to try and plan for the worst. When the RIT identifies a fireground hazard that may affect their ability to get their ultimate job done (successfully rescuing a firefighter in trouble) then they should attempt to eliminate the hazard. If the hazard can't be eliminated then it's critical that Command and Safety, as well as all firefighters operating on the fireground, know of the hazard. It's also critical that the hazard be factored into the overall RIT plan — should they be deployed.

ENSURING AN IMMEDIATE RIT RESPONSE

Ensuring an immediate response is the major function of the RIT. While all of the above proactive tasks should be done they must be done *simultaneous* to this one task. The bottom line is that a portion of the RIT must be able to immediately deploy if a firefighter is in trouble. That means that they must not be engaged in any other functions that would delay their response.

This is why staffing and training the RIT is so important. A minimum of four firefighters (six would be ideal) should make up the RIT. If two are performing proactive tasks then two (four with a six person RIT) are standing by — at the most likely entrance — to deploy. If the RIT is deployed then the members performing proactive tasks should immediately move to the point of entry and follow the RIT tag line. The RIT tag line will lead them to the rest of the team and the search effort can continue.

The bottom line regarding proactive RIT tasks on the fireground is that a portion of the RIT should perform proactive tasks to make potential RIT deployments successful — *while a portion of the RIT remains in a ready-mode to deploy*. If performing any of the proactive tasks would compromise the ability of the RIT to immediately deploy then Command must be notified. Additional resources should be requested to perform the tasks.

9

Responding to a MAYDAY – The RIT Deployment

Let's face it, you never know when or how it will happen! In fact, when you least expect it — expect it. Responding as part of the RIT — to a known firefighter MAYDAY — will be one of the most stressful situations you'll ever encounter as a firefighter. All previous training and preparation will be put to the test!

The skills used to search for and rescue a firefighter were discussed in previous chapters. All members must be proficient with these skills so they can *focus* on the bigger picture if an actual MAYDAY occurs.

RIT DEPLOYMENT

This is what it's all about, why you've done all the training and preparation. A firefighter is trapped, missing, disoriented, or has simply declared a MAYDAY with no additional information. *When it happens it won't be textbook.* What's important is that the RIT is deployed — immediately — to begin their search for the firefighter.

ENTRY

Where are you going? Who are you looking for? Where will you enter the building and begin the search? When the RIT is deployed it must get as much information as possible — LUNAR — and, combined with the previous information it has gathered, determine the best entry location. Once determined, the entry location should be announced — for Command, other members of the RIT who may have been performing proactive tasks, and additional RITs who will stage at the location awaiting further information.

Once at the entry point the RIT Officer should confirm the team assignments (Navigation/Air, Search, Packaging...) and brief the members on the *search plan* (initial direction, possible location, knowledge of PASS activation or any radio traffic from the victim, etc). All members should also make a quick check to ensure that all the equipment and tools needed for the search are assembled and ready to go. The Navigation/Air Supply firefighter should secure the tag line to the outside and the RIT Officer should benchmark that the RIT has entered the building.

The time from deployment to entry should be as short as possible. If the team is maintaining a ready-state, staged with the proper tools at the probable entry point, then it's simply a matter of masking up and starting the search. Remember, the clock is already ticking when the MAYDAY is declared — *the firefighter's already in trouble* — and time is running out.

SEARCH

During the search, maintain composure! Stick to the plan. Perform your assignment. The RIT Officer must determine the direction of travel and type of search to be used — this may change throughout the search. In addition, the RIT Officer must benchmark major changes in location (first floor, second floor, basement...). Don't forget to update Command and keep track of your crew.

The Search firefighters must aggressively search. Don't become a part of the problem by straying off from the rest of the crew. Be aggressive but be accountable. Search the area, communicate your findings, and move. *Remember, you're searching for a firefighter!*

If you're responsible for Navigation, manage the tag line. Keep the line tight when it's deployed. If you move in and out of a room then make sure the excess line is picked up and the slack is removed. Don't make an incoming RIT team follow 200 feet of line to move 70 feet into the building — manage the line.

Monitor your air supply — individually and as a team. Don't wait until your low air alarm starts sounding to start paying attention. Depending on where you are in the building you may have just become part of the problem. Call for an additional RIT before you're running out of air so that they can continue the search without delay.

Searching for, and locating, the firefighter is critical! The rescue can't start until the search is complete (the firefighter is found). Use any and all techniques available to find the firefighter.

ASSESSING, STABILIZING AND PACKAGING

When the firefighter is found it's time to switch gears from search to rescue. While assessing the firefighter, it's also important to make a quick assessment of the

fire and structural conditions, the RIT, and their air supply.

The RIT Officer should benchmark that the firefighter has been found, announce the RITs current location, request an additional RIT to help with the removal operation, and begin to develop the *rescue/removal plan*. If additional tools are needed to extricate the firefighter then they should be requested and brought in with the incoming RIT. Another possibility is that a hose line may be needed to protect the firefighter (and RIT) during the extrication/removal. The need for a hose line must be communicated immediately.

The Navigation/Air Supply firefighter, along with one of the Search firefighters (Packaging), should assess the firefighter's condition and secure his air supply. When the air supply is secured (benchmarked by the RIT Officer) the Navigation firefighter should secure the tag line in the area or hand it off to the RIT Officer to secure. The Packaging firefighter should continue preparing the firefighter for removal (tighten shoulder straps, convert harness, apply sling, etc.).

The other Search firefighter should perform a quick search of the area for any nearby windows or doors that can be used for immediate egress. If a potential exit point is found it should be communicated to the RIT Officer so it can be factored into the *rescue/removal plan.*

RESCUE

When the firefighter is ready to be removed (packaged, extricated) then it's time to implement the *rescue/removal plan.* The RIT Officer should benchmark the intended removal location so that additional help can be assembled. If it's an extended extrication then the RIT may act as support for a specialty team (collapse, etc.). An additional possibility is that the RIT can prepare an exit location while the specialty team is freeing the firefighter (rope-assisted, exterior wall breach, etc.).

When the firefighter is on the way out (the rescue is under way) the RIT Officer must maintain control and

discipline within the rescue team. Frustration will be high, adrenaline flowing, and tempers short — not to mention the fatigue — so clear communication and direction is a must.

If the *rescue/removal plan* calls for the firefighter to be removed along the tag line then the RIT Officer maintains the line behind the other RIT members as they remove the firefighter (drag, carry, etc.). The RIT Officer will be the last one out — keeping the line tight to provide the shortest and most direct route to the exit.

If the *rescue/removal plan* calls for the firefighter to be removed following a different route — or through a nearby window or door — then the tag line should be extended until the exit location is reached. At this point, the tag line may be deployed and managed by the RIT Officer or the Navigation firefighter (depending on his involvement in the actual removal process).

The RIT Officer should benchmark when the firefighter has been removed from the building and that the RIT team is accounted for.

REMEMBER THE BASICS

Before Entering...

- Confirm the MAYDAY information — LUNAR
- Confirm assignments
- Recall additional members who may be performing proactive tasks
- Announce the entry location
- Use a RIT tag line and attach it outside

When Searching...

- Have a plan — and follow it
- Communicate findings/location
- Bring the right equipment
- Search for a firefighter (it's different than a civilian search!)
- Monitor interior conditions
- Monitor air supply
- Don't become part of the problem
- Call for additional resources before needed
- Use any and all techniques to FIND the firefighter

When the Firefighter is Found

- Notify Command/Rescue

- Call for an additional RIT

- Assess the firefighter

- Assess the conditions

- Assess the RIT members

- Secure the firefighter's air supply

- Develop the rescue/removal plan

- Determine the best removal location

- Package the firefighter for removal

- Rescue/remove the firefighter

- Update Command/Rescue of progress

THE MAYDAY/RESCUE ENVIRONMENT

Nothing can prepare you for the *actual* conditions and stress that will accompany a lost, missing, or distressed firefighter emergency on the fireground. The fireground will be chaotic — to say the least! Discipline, developed through previous training and preparation, will play a role in the overall success of the mission.

10

Commanding
Rapid Intervention Operations

Commanding RIT operations is something that most departments don't have a lot of experience with. This is both a good thing and a bad thing. It's a good thing because RIT operations don't happen very often. It's a bad thing because when they do we don't know how to handle them. The end result of this lack of experience is that when an actual fireground emergency occurs, chaos results. When things go bad on the fireground, they really go bad. It seems like everything *snowballs* and even the simplest of tasks become almost impossible.

One thing that departments, and Incident Commanders, must realize is that when an emergency occurs on the fireground (a missing firefighter, a MAY-DAY, etc.) they will quickly be overwhelmed by the event. **The *Crisis Management techniques* that have worked in the past are no match for the events that will accompany a MAYDAY operation.**

Commanding a RIT operation requires advanced planning! It also requires:

- Trained firefighters

- A solid RIT SOP

- Adequate RIT resources on the fireground

- A strong Command structure

- Disciplined operations

- Solid communication

- A little bit of luck...

TRAINED FIREFIGHTERS

Let's face it, training is usually a low priority in the overall scheme of things. Sure, there are pockets of fire-fighters within every department that will stay on top of things but the majority of firefighters will have to be forced to train.

Staying proficient with basic firefighting operations—when the actual amount of fireground time continues to decline—is tough! Departments must come up with ways to keep members proficient.

Beyond the basics, all firefighters should be trained in individual firefighter survival skills, firefighter res-cue skills, and rapid intervention team operations.

Actually, many of these skills are just a *repackaged* version of basic firefighting skills — but the training must still be provided.

A SOLID RIT SOP

Develop one! Deploying a RIT to rescue a firefighter will be the most difficult thing your department has ever dealt with. If you're not prepared then things will get worse before they get better.

RIT operations are tough. They're chaotic. They're few and far between. They don't happen on every fireground, thankfully, so it's critical that department members have something to go by (an SOP). By taking the time to develop a RIT SOP, and training members on it, there's a much better chance of things going smooth when the time comes.

The RIT SOP should provide a *game plan* for RIT operations on the fireground. It should cover—among other things—dispatch, the team, tools, team positions, staging, proactive actions, communication, accountability, Command, additional resources, and benchmarks.

ADEQUATE RIT RESOURCES

This includes initial RIT resources as well as additional resources in the event that an actual emergency is declared.

Initial RIT Staffing

Staffing is a problem in almost every department. Not having enough personnel to handle the basic firefighting tasks certainly compounds problems when trying to staff a RIT. Unfortunately, there are no excuses when a firefighter is in trouble.

For those departments that have the staffing, make it a point to put the appropriate resources on the fireground at the outset. A fireground fatality when there's additional units available — that may have factored into the overall operations — is inexcusable.

For departments that don't have the staffing, take the time to develop mutual and automatic aid agreements with neighboring communities. Developing these relationships works for both departments and provides a safer fireground.

Multiple RITs (MAYDAY RIT Staffing)

In the event of an actual MAYDAY on the fireground RIT resources will be quickly exhausted *(a minimum of three teams will be needed to handle the emergency)*. Too many departments try and "nickel and dime" the additional resources needed by calling for one or two additional companies at a time.

Call for the next alarm assignment. If you're operating on a first alarm then call for a second alarm. At the very least place the companies in staging. Playing catch-up doesn't work!

A STRONG COMMAND STRUCTURE

The Incident Commander will not be able to run the fire and the RIT operations — it's too much! Communication breaks down. Discipline breaks down. What's already a bad situation continues to get worse because there's just too much going on.

Develop a Rescue Sector on the fireground that is responsible for the RIT operation. Command must continue to focus on the actual incident and Rescue will focus on the RIT operation. As with all operations, and successful Incident Command Systems, the positions must be staffed by qualified individuals. Don't just throw another box in the ICS organizational chart— train personnel ahead of time to manage RIT operations.

The proactive approach would be to have a Rescue Sector from the outset — but that requires additional resources that departments either don't have or are unwilling to commit. At the very least, have a system in place that immediately establishes a Rescue Sector, calls for additional RIT resources, and provides the best possible chance for success.

DISCIPLINED OPERATIONS

Disciplined operations come from training and preparation. In addition, a strong Command structure and accountability system help maintain discipline on the fireground. When a firefighter is in trouble everyone on the fireground will want to help — that's understandable. However, if everyone drops what they're doing to try and help out with the rescue operation then the fire conditions (and fireground) will continue to deteriorate. During active fireground conditions both the RIT and the fire control operations must occur simultaneously.

A breakdown of discipline during RIT operations will jeopardize the entire fireground — and ultimately risk the success of the mission!

SOLID COMMUNICATIONS

LUNAR

Last known location?

Unit number?

Name?

Assignment?

Radio equipped?

Communication is a constant problem on the fireground. Sometimes it's the equipment and sometimes it's us. Training on fireground communication is almost non-existent *(who needs to train on that?).*

Communication is vital to all fireground operations and during a RIT operation it's even more important. There is critical information that must be relayed if the operation is to be successful.

Who is in trouble? Where are they? What happened? Where did the RIT enter? Where is the RIT? What problems are they encountering? What is the status of the RIT members? When the firefighter is found what is his condition? Is extrication required? Can the initial RIT make the rescue?

RIT Communication Benchmarks

The RIT should provide certain benchmarks during the operation. At a minimum the benchmarks should include:

- RIT entry and location
- RIT location changes — first floor, second floor...
- Firefighter located
- Air supply secured

WHAT ABOUT SWITCHING RADIO CHANNELS?

One question that often comes up when talking about RIT operations and radio communications is — *should the RIT (or everyone else on the fireground) switch to another radio channel?* There's no easy answer to this question. Some departments do it and some don't. There are certainly advantages and disadvantages to splitting up the operating forces onto different channels. *Training is the key!*

During a fireground emergency there will be a lot of radio traffic (especially if department members lack radio discipline). The chance of missing critical information from, or about, the missing firefighter may affect the overall outcome. *During an emergency, all information is important.* Having multiple channels will definitely reduce the amount of radio traffic on the main channel. A possible downside to this is that some members may not hear the message to switch or they may inadvertently switch to the wrong channel. Now, when attempting to contact those members on the wrong channel it may result in an additional *lost* firefighter situation. When deciding whether or not to go to another radio channel consider the following?

- Are there channels available?
- Will all members hear the message to switch?
- Will additional emergencies result if members are unable to contact one another after switching?

Providing radio and communications training and instilling radio discipline among members will positively impact any fireground—especially during RIT operations.

- Removal location
- Firefighter removed
- RIT out of building

In addition, time updates should be given to keep the RIT informed and to assist them in monitoring their search time and air supply.

A LITTLE BIT OF LUCK...

As we said at the beginning, there's no doubt that luck plays a role in any successful firefighter rescue but the commitment of the individual firefighters and the entire department plays a more important role.

Supporting a firefighter rescue and rapid intervention team program requires more than simply writing it down and providing a 'lip service' response, it requires a conscious effort on the part of all involved—along with frequent and realistic training—to be prepared for whatever might happen.

PART III

FIREFIGHTER RESCUE & RIT TRAINING SESSIONS

Firefighter Rescue & Rapid Intervention Team Training Sessions

Training for firefighter rescue and rapid intervention team operations should be frequent and ongoing. In addition to this type of training, firefighters should continually review and practice individual firefighter survival skills as well as basic engine and truck company operations. The more proficient members are at performing the basics, the less likely they are to get into trouble during normal operations.

In the event that trouble does arise, firefighters — and departments — who are proficient at performing firefighter rescue and rapid intervention team operations will have a much greater chance of success.

DESIGNING TRAINING SESSIONS

When designing training sessions for firefighter rescue and rapid intervention teams it's important to build a solid foundation and progress from basic to advanced.

Teach the individual firefighter rescue techniques and let the students practice them and become proficient. Start by giving a demonstration of the techniques and then letting the students practice them while wearing all of their gear, including their SCBA (not breathing air). Once the students become proficient at performing the skills, increase the level of difficulty by breathing air and reducing the visibility (black-out masks, wax paper, etc.). Finally, when the students have developed a level of proficiency incorporate more realistic conditions — smoke, heat, noise — so they can see how difficult it will be on the fireground.

Once the students have become proficient at performing the individual firefighter rescue skills it's time to start incorporating them into actual RIT operations. Remember, performing the actual rescue is only part of the overall RIT function.

RIT training sessions should incorporate all aspects of the RIT — size-up, proactive tasks, performing the rescue — and should progress from basic to advanced. Don't start out by throwing a full-scale building collapse

TRAINING IN FIREGROUND CONTEXT

Training sessions should first focus on individual skills and then focus on complete RIT evolutions. Once you're comfortable performing the skills then practice them in the *fireground context,* the conditions you're likely to face during a true emergency.

Fireground context includes:

- Full personal protective clothing.
    - That means all of your turnout gear.
    - Firefighting gloves, not leather work gloves.
    - A hood on and in place.
- SCBA with PASS device armed.
    - Breathing off of the SCBA, not just wearing it.
    - If the PASS device chirps, move.
- Blacked-out SCBA face piece (or smoke).
- Realistic fireground noise.
    - Water flowing, glass breaking, smoke detectors beeping, radio transmissions, engines running, chain saws operating, fans operating, and any other fireground sounds you're likely to encounter.
- Realistic fireground activities.

While everyone can't be performing the rescue and RIT skills at the same time, make them review fireground basics — engine and truck company operations required to bring the fire under control.

scenario at the students — with multiple companies missing — and expect positive results!

Start with the basics. A residential fire with a fire-fighter missing (or disoriented) is a realistic starting point. Again, as the students progress the level of difficulty should increase. More advanced scenarios might include partial collapse or entanglement requiring the RIT to extricate the firefighter. This increases the amount of time needed and stresses the need for more resources.

As training advances begin to incorporate more difficult structures — commercial buildings, apartment buildings, etc. — and challenges (multiple RITs, large-area search techniques, etc). Remember, a RIT operation could occur at any time on any fireground — train for all possibilities!

SAFETY IN TRAINING

All training should be done under the guidance of a qualified trainer. All safety measures must be in place when performing any training skills. All training that involves rescuer/victim removals from upper floors should include life safety lines and harnesses. **While the risk of injury still exists—the alternative to not performing this type of training is far more costly.**

FIREFIGHTER RESCUE TRAINING SESSIONS

Firefighter rescue training sessions should concentrate on developing proficiency with the individual skills (search, packaging, securing air supply, etc.) and not an entire RIT operation.

Searching for a Firefighter

FIREFIGHTER MISSING WITH PASS ACTIVATED

The RIT should perform an aggressive search of the occupancy (residential/commercial) in an attempt to locate a missing firefighter by moving toward an activated PASS device. The missing firefighter does not respond to his radio and his assignment and last known location are unknown. Once located the firefighter should be removed to the outside.

RADIO-ASSISTED SEARCH – NO PASS

The RIT should perform an aggressive search of the occupancy (residential/commercial) in an attempt to locate a missing firefighter by moving toward the squelching sound of his radio — created when the search team uses a radio-assisted technique. The missing firefighter does not respond to his radio (it is turned on), his PASS device is not sounding and his assignment and last known location are unknown. Once located the firefighter should be removed to the outside.

BASIC LARGE AREA SEARCH

The RIT, given a large open-area warehouse, should perform an aggressive search using a guide line and individual search lines (large area search system) to locate the firefighter. The missing firefighter's PASS device is sounding but his assignment and last known location are unknown. Once located the firefighter should be removed to the outside.

FIREFIGHTER MISSING NO ADDITIONAL INFORMATION

The RIT, given only that there is a firefighter missing in the structure (residential/commercial), uses any combination of techniques to locate the firefighter. The missing firefighter does not respond to his radio (it is turned on), his PASS device is sounding and his assignment and last known location are unknown. Once located the firefighter should be removed to the outside.

Assessing, Stabilizing and Packaging a Firefighter

ASSESSING A DOWNED FIREFIGHTER

After locating a downed firefighter and resetting his PASS device, perform an initial assessment. During the assessment confirm that the firefighter is breathing, that there is air flowing to his face piece, and the amount of air remaining in his SCBA. If any entanglements are found, that can easily be removed, remove them. *The RIT members should be blacked-out throughout the scenario.*

SECURING THE AIR SUPPLY — NEARBY WINDOW

Several scenarios can be conducted that allow RIT members to secure the air supply of a downed firefighter.

- Moving the firefighter into a window
- Establishing a buddy breathing connection
- Using a RIT Air Pack — regulator swap, UAC connection, face piece exchange

SECURING AND CONVERTING THE SCBA HARNESS

RIT members should secure the SCBA of a downed firefighter by tightening the shoulder straps and converting the waist strap into an improvised harness.

APPLYING A SLING OR WEBBING TO MOVE A FIREFIGHTER

After locating a downed firefighter, RIT members should secure a piece of webbing or a sling device to assist dragging the firefighter out of the structure.

Rescue and Removal Techniques

DISENTANGLEMENT AND REMOVAL

Members should become proficient at freeing an unconscious firefighter who is found entangled in debris (fallen wires, suspended ceiling gridwork, HVAC ductwork, etc.). The debris should be removed from the immediate area so that it doesn't cause a problem during the removal.

EXTRICATION FROM INTERIOR COLLAPSE

Members should become proficient at extricating a firefighter from an interior collapse that requires lifting (and shoring) debris to access and remove the firefighter. An important part of this scenario is learning what amount/type of collapse can be handled by the RIT and what amount/type requires a collapse team.

DRAGS AND CARRIES

Firefighters should practice moving a downed firefighter using a variety of drags and carries. Include SCBA drags, webbing/sling drags, tool drags, and rope drags. Carries should also be practiced (two firefighter, pike pole).

UP AND DOWN STAIRS

Firefighters should practice moving firefighters up and down stairs. Both two and three person lifts should be practiced. For the ultimate test, and eye-opener, firefighters should attempt to remove their partner from a basement (up a flight of stairs) before the RIT arrives to assist.

WINDOW RESCUES

The various window rescue techniques should be practiced so that a number of options are available depending on the fireground conditions and the size of the victim. Practice:

- Removing a firefighter from a first-floor window
- Lifting a firefighter into a second-floor window
- Carrying a firefighter down a ladder from a second-floor window
- Lowering an unconscious firefighter using a high-point pulley system and a 2:1 mechanical advantage system
- Performing the Denver drill (both inside positions and the outside position)

RESCUES FROM BELOW — THE NANCE DRILL

Practice various methods of accessing a firefighter who has fallen through the floor to a lower level. Once the firefighter has been accessed, practice using the handcuff knot(s) to raise both the firefighter and the victim out of the hole.

RAPID INTERVENTION TEAM TRAINING SESSIONS

While some of the RIT training sessions may seem to duplicate the skills performed during the firefighter rescue training sessions it's important to remember that the RIT skills are performed as part of a complete scenario. The firefighter rescue sessions concentrated on the individual skills (and did not include all aspects of a RIT operation).

Team Positions

THE RIT OFFICER

All members should act as the RIT Officer during an entire RIT scenario. The leadership and communication skills needed to perform these types of operations cannot be developed without participating in realistic training.

NAVIGATION/AIR SUPPLY

Deploying and managing a tag line while transporting the RIT air pack and operating under realistic fireground conditions is an essential part of RIT operations. This position requires constant training to develop proficiency. All members should act as the Navigation/Air Supply member during an entire RIT scenario.

SEARCH

Speed is critical when searching for a firefighter! The search component of RIT operations is often overlooked as an area that needs constant training. Search members must be aggressive but accountable. All members should act in the Search position during an entire RIT scenario.

RIT Tools and Staging

Determining the proper location and then properly setting up a RIT staging area are prerequisites for any successful RIT operation. The complacent nature of fire-ground RIT operations, along with the limited staffing of most departments, causes these critical steps to be hastily performed, or omitted all together.

All members should select a proper location (based on a given scenario) and set up a RIT (with the tools staged) staging area for the following structures:

- Residence
- Commercial warehouse
- Multi-story (3 or more floors) structure with crews operating on upper floors

Proactive RIT Tasks

RADIO MONITORING, COMPANY ACCOUNTABILITY, AND TACTICAL WORKSHEET

Given an audio tape of a previous incident (combining it with available video or still images would be helpful), RIT members should monitor radio traffic and create/update a RIT Tactical Worksheet indicating companies, assignments, locations, potential hazards/problems, availability of on-scene apparatus and additional equipment, and alternative access/egress locations.

360° SURVEY OF FIREGROUND

Working as part of RIT, and while maintaining a portion of the RIT in a ready-state to begin searching, a 360° survey of the fireground should be conducted. The findings should be transferred to the RIT Tactical Worksheet and a rescue plan developed.

LADDERING THE FIREGROUND FOR RIT

Working as part of RIT, and while maintaining a portion of the RIT in a ready-state to begin searching, the fireground should be laddered on all sides.

REMOVING WINDOW BARS

Working as part of RIT, and while maintaining a portion of the RIT in a ready-state to begin searching, security bars should be removed from windows located on both the first and second floors of a structure.

REMOVING HUD/BOARDED WINDOWS

Working as part of RIT, and while maintaining a portion of the RIT in a ready-state to begin searching, plywood coverings should be removed from windows located on both the first and second floors of a structure.

FORCIBLE ENTRY

Working as part of RIT, and while maintaining a portion of the RIT in a ready-state to begin searching, various forcible entry challenges should be dealt with — roll down security doors, scissor gates, chained entrances.

The RIT Deployment

REGROUP AND DEPLOY

The RIT should respond to a fireground MAYDAY and activation (from Command) by choosing the best entry location, announcing the entry location, recalling RIT members performing proactive tasks, and beginning the RIT search for the firefighter.

As RIT members who were performing proactive tasks arrive at the entry location they should announce their entry into the building and the point when they reach the interior RIT.

Members should perform both positions — team ready to search and team being recalled from performing proactive tasks.

RIT Scenarios

This is what it all comes down to — performing as a RIT during a full-scale fireground emergency with firefighters lost/disoriented, missing, or trapped. This is also where departments learn that having one RIT on the scene is — in most cases — not going to be enough to get the job done.

Set up a number of scenarios — complete with smoke conditions and realistic fireground noises and challenges — that will force RITs to work under intense conditions to search for and rescue a downed firefighter.

The scenarios are limited only by your imagination. What is extremely important is to create realistic conditions. **Don't set them up to fail — just let them operate under conditions likely to be encountered on the street — success or failure depends on**

training and preparation. There is no need to add unrealistic problems into the scenarios, the members of the RIT will create their own problems that will have to be dealt with and overcome if the rescue is to be successful.

TRAINING SAVES LIVES FIREFIGHTERS

"In the heat of battle you don't remember very much. You don't think very fast. You act by instinct, which is really training. So you've got to be trained for battle so that you will react exactly the way you did in training."

Admiral Arleigh Burke, U.S. Navy

NOTES

NOTES

NOTES